MUSICAL CHRONICLE
(1917--1923)

BY

PAUL ROSENFELD

NEW YORK
HARCOURT, BRACE AND COMPANY

COPYRIGHT, 1923, BY
HARCOURT, BRACE AND COMPANY, INC.

PRINTED IN THE U. S. A. BY
THE QUINN & BODEN COMPANY
RAHWAY, N. J.

TO

ALFRED STIEGLITZ

The greater portion of the material of which this book is composed has been printed in the form of articles in *Arts and Decoration, The Dial, The New Republic, The Seven Arts,* and *Vanity Fair;* and thanks are due the editors of these periodicals for permission to reprint it. Most of the chapters have been thoroughly recobbled, and a good many have been completely re-written; in the effort not of assembling them about a single point of view, but of more accurately expressing the feelings with which they were originally conceived.

CONTENTS

MUSICAL CHRONICLE

Prologue to the Annual Tragedy

MIDSUMMER is not passed before the pestiferous unwelcome hunger gnaws again. Before a twig has turned, it's full awake in you, the damned appetite for concerts, mounting to the skull, enfeebling the silly eye and making it to perceive in the wintry distances, where only frozen fields extend, a dance of golden soloists, a pageant of purple orchestras. But a few weeks since you had thought yourself rid of it forever, and exchanged happy handshakes with yourself on having escaped its fearful clutch. Springtide had found you disabused, a cool and angry shoulder presented to the concert hall. By night the foyer lights might shine, and ladies in red velvet enter in: you were not to be lured to follow on. Had God himself upon the trombone been advertised for only and positively farewell appearance, not even a fainting desire to hear him would have flickered.

You had had enough; enough for always, it seemed. No more would lust for dulcet sounds in concert send you to expend your treasure, to waste many a good evening, and return homeward destroyed. Since there was so little opportunity for satisfactions, stoical resignation had entered in, it seemed, and anesthetized desire. A voice from above had whispered that in all the future years, two or at the most three concerts every year would satisfy completely all the craving left, and unending disappointment no longer be the portion. A respectable quantity of income hitherto charmed under false pretenses into the pouches of managers would

3

henceforward be free to find a slower and better way into
the pockets of tobacco merchants. And, sitting by the
fire, a calmful eye upon Plato's book or Gibbon's, you
would let the unilluminated struggle through rain and
sleet to Polyhymnia's tomb; and smile, and have the
better part.

But every summer, the ninth month, arriving, finds you
in the boots of the wretch without the price of a dinner,
who purchases himself a cake of cheap chocolate in the
hope of deceiving his belly, and but a few hours after he
has congratulated himself on the extinction of his hunger,
finds it gnawing furiously. The accumulated mass of the
unhappy experiences of many musical seasons; the disillusionment with the whole poor business of music-
making, has no weight. You surprise yourself dreaming
blandly forward toward the coming concert-studded
winter, toward the cool weather time when you can go
hear people sing and play. Symphonies to come draw
stately through the imagination. The horns of Elfland,
Philadelphia, and Boston are heard faintly blowing. Forgotten entirely is the last bad performance of the "Jupiter" of Mozart or the Fourth of Brahms. The first of
the conductors to announce either for performance will
have you at his heels. There is no time you glide upon
the autobus down Fifty-seventh street that the black and
red placards framed on the walls of Carnegie Hall do not
thrill with the promise of auricularly blissful autumn
hours. The prospectuses of the various organizations
transmitted through the mails excite with their dazzling
announcements of premières, revivals, soloists, historical
cycles, guest-conductorships, festivals. In trembling and
in haste is the check prepared which will prevent sub-
scription-seats becoming forfeit, and doors being shut
upon you the night the bridegroom cometh. You even

catch yourself turning to the exclamatory irregular blocks in the daily press where, during the season, managers announce, present, and have the honor of offering foremost American pianists, greatest Russian violinists, Jewish Carusi, boy-prodigies from Austria, girl-prodigies from Brazil, pupils of Auer and protégées of Lambert, Griffes Groups, Beethoven Associations, Damrosch festivals and all-Tchaikowsky programs. It is not even in the hope of finding that some major artist is announcing an out-of-season concert, that you have done so. You have peeped, oh, shame, in the mere hope of finding that the proximate appearance of some one of the daffodils that come before the swallow dares, and take the applause of October with too many encores, is advertised.

Galeotto is not the fickleness of the human mind. Galeotto is the summer, which removes the concerts, and brings you close to the spirit of music. Galeotto is the country, which wakes into play faculties which the city atrophies, and opens the being to rhythm. The city is preponderantly mental; the modern city especially. It is built *more geometrico;* all hard right angles and straight lines; all unrhythmical regularity and no rhythmical interplay of the mechanical and the free. The light is interrupted by buildings. The skies are remote and piecemeal. The spring is choked under pavements when it comes. The life in the city seems to mould itself on the sharp corners and hard insensitive lines. One lives in the head. One lives all the time on capital amassed over the summer, and most often the balance is dangerously low. But the country is irregular and free. It is all unpremeditable curve and growing, flowing, vagrant substance, and live and fluttering green. You do not have to squeeze this bit of nightblue over high cornices, this wistful North River scape, glimpsed between chasm sides, to get relief from the ubiquitous mechanical. The open sky, the back of the hill, the fantasy of the thrusting boughs, have it for you in generous open hands. Things move in strange free patterns. A kingfisher skims sudden and swift, instantaneous gray and white, over the sheet of the pond. Stars large as sunbursts hang their soft rich beams out of fathomless blacknesses which no city-lights flush with sachet-rose. And life moves a little like the running vines on crumbling pasture walls—like the clouds chasing high and schoolboyish through limitless blue.

At a turn of a road where meadows extend and elms and beeches spread, Beethoven can stand awaiting you. For art is the combination of the geometrical mechanical element which lives in modern cities with the unpremeditable, vagrant element of the unadorned land. It is the combination of the straight line and the scattering dots. All his little day, man is striving to synchronize with the great rhythm that pulses outside him, in the earth, in the air. All the time, he is seeking to give himself to that rhythm, to inhale and to exhale with the breathing of the earth, to leap into the dance and let the dance be the inner movement of him. Life must go swinging and balanced and graceful as it goes where blue and white acrobats flit from trapeze to trapeze under the canvas circus-vault. And out of his yearning, there comes art. For what happens to the most of us only at rare intervals of time: synchronization in the universal rhythms, pacification, cleansing, and release, happens often to the men we call artists. Philosophies, poems, symphonies, bulging rich canvases, they are there to record those moments of coincidence.

Lucky you are if you have music by you in the open. For, as one who has never read a poem out of doors cannot quite know what a poem may be, so one who has never heard music played in the open, and not alone in parks or gardens, but among lush and wild-growing plants, cannot quite know how deep it can enter in. Never to have heard a Brahms quartet out of doors in the evening when the hillsides flow softly as vineyards winding away in the distance, and the village standpipe appears a donjon in the gloaming; never to have heard the faëry scherzo dissolve with the familiar rims and contours, among gray bushes and misted meadows, while the last greenish light follows the long since sunken sun, is never entirely to have felt the shy life, the subdued passion, the grave sweet reconciliation in the music. No one can quite comprehend modern music who has not had a piano far away from houses in a hut in the sun-warmed woods, by rocks and balsam and sumach; and there turned from the endless concertizing, the never-ceasing rhythming of tree-toads, crickets, and rustling leafage to the wild free numbers of the new composers; and again, after playing, returned once more to the soughing of the wind, the creaking of the laden branches, the pauses of brooding fecund silence, the smell of cones, needles and fallen leaves, the flicker of the light on the red-gold ground.

So, strapping from tramps, swims, games, you are ready for the dionysiac fiddler. He must play up. You are ready for the Seventh Symphony of Beethoven and the seventh of all the musicians. You have inside you the touchstone of music. Hence, the midsummer music-madness. From the débris of the seasons, a few perfect experiences last over to you. Forgetting the innumerable instances when performances took away rather more than gave, when they debauched rather more than fulfilled, you remember only the moments scattered over many years when compositions suddenly reared enormous over you, when the moon-worship of the music breathed, and the great winds and tides swept through the hall. You remember an hour when Harold Bauer, for instance, sat and played Sebastian stately at the clavichord; when Casals brushed Velasquez tones across his 'cello-bridge; when Ornstein unfurled the sensuous stuffs of Debussy; or Mengelberg splashed Flemish sunshine Hals-like about Carnegie Hall and made the trombones blare kirmess-carousal; or Stokowski let go; and the Society of the Friends of Music befriended music indeed. For you are with music, not with musicians. You have seen the bourne of all music, and the fact of the interfering concert-hall and the personalities of the performers is forgotten. The music exists so fully that it seems incredible anything should prevent it realizing itself quite effortlessly and perfectly. An ocean is about to be discharged. The dry dusty banks get the semblance of saturation. The gray air under the smoky cloudbanks is veiled in blushful mists. You are about to be launched into abundance.

True, the midsummer music-madness doesn't persist very long. By the time the first trump has sounded, it is dying. You have but to get a whiff of the concert-hall, to sit one minute in a seat in the waiting rows, to know the truth again. It becomes plain again that he who makes so bold as to enter a concert-hall without carrying with him an interesting book with which, as soon as it becomes necessary, he can while away the time, is nothing more than a ninny.

Without indulging in special thaumaturgical practices of any kind, without examining the entrails of any musical bird, you know exactly what is going to take place during the oncoming season. You know that what is going to happen is very much the same that happened last season; and that was next to nothing at all. There is no music to be had. Millions are going to be spent for pretense, and not one cent for living tribute. The profession of conductors will do heroic work as usual in preventing symphonies of any composers save Tschaikowsky and Brahms from being heard. A neglected overture of Beethoven's, the "Leonore" No. III, will be dragged forth twelve or fourteen times from an unjust oblivion. A little-known poem of Rimsky's named "Scheherazade" will be presented several times to an astounded public. When President Masaryk, the republic of Czecho-Slovakia, the Philharmonic Society or Conductor Stransky has a birthday, there will take place the première of a brilliant and revolutionary work, by one Dvorák, called the "Symphony from the New World." Several apprentice works by ultra-modern composers will be presented, which will give the critics an opportunity of announcing triumphantly that there's nothing as original in Snougorowski and Rimmelsharp as people pretend. If by chance a really representative modern work is performed, it will be performed so badly that its sharpest denigrators will find themselves overwhelmingly justified. When Albert Coates arrives from London to take the wand from the hand of Walter the Pitiless, he will surely do An Episode in the Life of a Very Old Gentleman, vulgarly known as "Le Poème de l'Extase." On the mouldering citadel of Wagner lies Bodansky like a thing of green bronze; he will conduct the "Walküre" so inspiredly that she will sound an elder sister of "Madama Butterfly." As for the glorious company of the pianists, there's not a one of that exalted confraternity who won't be found playing the Chopin b-minor sonata and all its faithful attendants. If one of them does the Opus 111 of Beethoven, all will do the Opus 111 of Beethoven.

Of course, a few surprises are certain to reward you before the ordeal of the winter is over. A few concerts will again issue you forth delighted and refreshed. Nevertheless, the best of music will come to you not in public places, but at some moment that finds you at the pianoforte, or in the room of some composer or true musician who has just stepped to his instrument with the wish of sharing with you something he has written or discovered. And yet, oh, sorrow, in spite of knowledge, here you are once again, sitting at a concert. The wheel of winter music-making spins you as before. You knew so well last spring what lay in store. But last summer overthrew your mind. And swoopingly, there comes the sense that next spring you will once more be cured by disgust; and next summer once again have a relapse. Many springs it will happen, and many summers.

Some day, of course, your fool will will renounce entirely the channel of recitals and music-making and develop some other spillway not so hopelessly choked by matter in the wrong place. That you know. Some day, you will have learned. As one grows older, it seems, one becomes less and less dependent upon other people for entertainment. One begins to be able to coincide once or twice oneself. But it is a pity that it takes this desirable state so many years to arrive. Every man learns to live. But by that time, he is seventy years of age at least.

August, 1921.

Rolland and the Composers

THE music books first set before Romain Rolland in his father's house in Clamecy contained little pieces by Mozart and Beethoven. When the lad was ill with some childish disease and afraid of death, it happened often that a melody of Mozart's came and watched like a beloved at his bedside and gave him comfort. There was a melody of Beethoven's which returned upon him in states of depression during his school years in Paris, and started the spark of eternal light in him again. In hours when the spirit of the student of the *Ecole Normale* lay withered and prone in illimitable dust, the piano and the old collections of German music quickened him along the length of his being as water, divided, quickens the body of the swimmer.

Music has never ceased from the work commenced upon the boy in the still house in Burgundy. The intercourse begun during his first lessons in piano playing has brought life to Rolland all his days. The form assumed by his spirit has come to it through the composers; there is scarcely one of his books which does not transmit to us, like sound carried from mystical distances, the drumming of the "Heroic" Symphony, the pure murmur of Bach and Schubert and Mozart's song. "Jean-Christophe" is a child begotten on the land of France by Beethoven's might of soul. "Colas Breugnon" is a scherzo, a Puckish ironical dance laid between a deep-flowing adagio and a grim heroic finale. "Beethoven," "Handel," and the other portraits of musicians are prose moulded, almost,

11

on musical style. Not only Rolland's books manifest the presence in his system of the composers. His work of character, too, vibrates with their rhythms. The place held by him throughout the war trumpets Beethoven no less than the biography does; and gives forth once again the stubborn human faith, the yearning for justice and love, the passionate appeal to the spirit in man, which cries through the symphonies, the "Solemn Mass," and the sonatas. It is just, that, at the conclusion of "Jean-Christophe," Rolland should have turned to the muse of the honey-colored hair no differently than, at the lucid close of life one might turn to a glorious love; just, that he should have inscribed the final section with words of the song with which Franz Schubert thanked the art of music for the unspeakable gift of the heart: "Du holde Kunst, wie dank' ich Dir dafür!" The freedom he has gotten, the grave fine personality into which he has grown, have come to him through his relations with the composers. In giving life to them, he has gotten it in exchange. Without musical art, there might well have been no high figure like the one we call by Rolland's name.

Music has been experience to him. Music has been penetration of consciousness of larger truth; widening of his own sense of the world with the senses of other men; intuition of Germany and the rest of Europe. For he has heard, always, as musicians do. The true musicians do not hear fifths and sevenths and ninths. The composers do not hear ascending figures and descending figures. Let Wagner teach you in what manner they hear each other's work. Wagner's essay on Beethoven includes a couple of pages on the c-minor quartet of the master; it is with these words that he commences his attempt at communicating what the composition of the dead man signifies to him:

I would like to compare the long introductory adagio, perhaps the most despondent matter ever expressed in tones, with
the awakening in the morning to a day "destined in its long
course to bring no wish, not a single one, to fulfillment."

It is with these words that he concludes the description:

We see him (Beethoven) looking out into life, wondering,
apparently (short adagio 3/4), how he is to go about the
business of making dance music for this world. There comes
a brief but melancholy moment of revery: it is as though he
had lost himself in the deepest dream of his mind. A glance
has shown him the core of the earth again. He awakes, and
moves his finger amid the strings in a dance rhythm such as
life has never before been given to hear (allegro finale). This
is the very dance of the earth: wild desire, woeful lamentation,
ecstasy of love, utmost bliss, misery, frenzy, voluptas and
pain. Lightnings beat here; thunders roll. And over all,
there stands the monstrous musician, compelling and moving
all things, proud and contained; guiding them from the rock-
ing sky down to the whirling earth and into the deepest abyss;
smiling at himself a little, since all this sorcery is to him nothing more than play.

And, in the whole long pages, not one of the phrases dear
to the estheticians.

No more than Wagner has Rolland been arrested by
the forms of the compositions presented to him. The
surging and the falling of the phrases, the interplay of
the beats, the sumptuousness of harmonies, all the wings
of musical art, have invariably carried him past the boun-
dary of surfaces into hidden formless lands. They have
carried him into regions where the eyes in the head do
not see, and where only the breast has sight; and there
placed him body to body with looming greatness and

sweetness and tenderness. They have left him groping
his way into beauties and loftiness new entirely to him.
He has returned into the day with knowledge and certainty of states of life he had not when he left it for the unknown. What life has given men other than himself has
suddenly become plain to him. He has seen one of them in
friendless solitude; and meeting his solitude without bitterness. He has seen men waiting for something; and men
praying; and men running through the emerald fields of
May frightening the cattle with their joy. It is as though
a door had been thrust through a wall, and given him egress
into a room wherein he had never been, and given it him
to become as familiar with the furniture it contained as
he was with that in his own chamber. It has gone with
him much as he has let it go with Christophe. Christophe
in his callower days sees chiefly the periwig when he hears
the works of J. S. Bach. But in loneliness and sickness
in Paris, the door of a body of music gives to his pressure.
And he sees the world of Bach. He hears the soul of the
little man

"roaring like a sea; hurricanes, winds howling, the clouds of
life scudding—men and women drunk with joy, sorrow, fury;
and the Christ, all meekness, the Prince of Peace, hovering
above them; towns awakened by the cries of the watchman,
running with glad shouts to meet the divine Bridegroom, whose
footsteps shake the earth; the vast store of thoughts, passions,
musical forms, heroic life, Shakespearean hallucinations, Sa-
vonarolaesque prophecies; pastoral, epic, apocalyptical visions,
all contained in the stout body of the little Thuringian cantor,
with his double chin, and little shining eyes under the wrinkled
lids and the raised eyebrows—he could see him so clearly!
sombre, jovial, a little absurd, with his head stuffed full of
allegories and symbols, Gothic and rococo; choleric, obstinate,
serene, with a passion for life and a great longing for death."

For life has come to Christophe; and increased itself
through some books printed with notes.

For Rolland has let himself feel music with his whole
man. He has let it break down the walls of his little
personal self, just as once in Clamecy it broke them down
in ridding him of fear; and delivered him from the
prison into which the world thrusts the sensitive spirit.
He has a kind of knowledge of works had by the creators
themselves. For, like them, he sees a portion of his own
stuff, some portion which society perhaps will not permit
him to realize, held before him through the work. There
is much of Beethoven, Berlioz, Handel, in the visions of
musicians which have risen before him. But there is just
as much of Romain Rolland in them; elements of his
nature which because of their kinship to what the music
expresses, have been unified by it and given a direction
into life. The heroic element of his being invariably
informs the visions. The heroic song in him, the courage
to have intense joy and pain, the passion which lifts life
into battle for an idea, the knowledge that "all greatness
is good, and the height of sorrow tops deliverance," utters
itself through them. Because of the high Alpine breath in
it, Péguy recognized in "Beethoven" a "great moral fortune" befallen France; and the clear high air is in all the
musical biographies. The timidity of the child, the frailty
of body of the man, may have resisted the broad gusts.
The state of France bore against it, certainly: helped hold
the self in within its small personal confines. For France,
with its gold-stockings, feared everything involving risk,
involving upset; encouraged "mediocrity in sorrow and
joy, selfish and niggardly suffering that has not the
strength to be rid of the lost pleasure, and in secret lends
itself to every sort of degradation to steal pleasure anew";
for mediocrity plays safe while intensity is perilous. But

music brought with it the rhythm of revolutionary and heroical ages. It brought the clamors and cries of men who dared accept their human heritage and be passionate and suffer and rejoice and love.

Music has broken down about Rolland many walls raised by education and environment; released many captive generosities. Not alone with its gold-stocking had French society tried to drive in on themselves the interests of the young people. The war of 1870, the Dreyfus case, were permitted to encourage a sort of mediocrity of soul. For they were permitted to case the mind about with a fear of the outer world and the foreigner; and shrink with ego with the religion of nationalism, masked expression of the insane regard for self. Some of the best minds of the generation were wounded by this military mysticism, or mystical militarism. The soul that was to achieve itself had to break through the web of nationalistic ritual spread for it. Of these meshes, too, music cut Rolland free. It showed him the lie of patriotism; cut the way for faith in life and love of the human creature. Its history showed him that the human mind had developed in spite of national boundaries; that it was in the interplay of a half dozen of peoples that musical art had grown; and that for the soul, there was no single country. It made him see eye to eye with Dehmel when he said

> Zehn Völkern schuldet meine Stirn
> Ihr bischen Hirn.

And musical art itself broke down prejudices in him by showing him the human being. The language spoken by it is international. In it speaks the place in the human being within whose confines idiomatic speech does not exist. It carries cries from a thousand different throats, from under a thousand different suns. And these cries from a thousand different throats and from under a thousand different suns are comprehensible wherever they fall. For the cries are but a single cry; in every human heart the same.

So, at the summons of the composers, what is robust and eager to be diverted in Rolland has many times broken the bands fastened by education and environment, and in the wedge of an image thrust its way into the world. Sometimes, it has come toward us wearing the traits of Beethoven or Michael Angelo or Tolstoy, and filled the sour air of Paris and the rest of the capital cities with the goodly aroma of grandeur of heart, of sorrow borne amid great emprises, of largeness of appetite and grasp. Sometimes, when it has chanced that the matter produced by the stimulus has contained more of Rolland himself than of the composers, the image has come wearing the traits of an imaginary, a composite musician; added itself to the material gathered about the name "Jean-Christophe Krafft"; and as in the biographies illuminated the stagnancy of modern civilization with the fire of human greatness. The novel is indeed a sort of sum of Rolland's experiences with music. Beethoven, Handel, Wagner, Hugo Wolf are present in it more intensely than in the sketches of their lives; and Rolland's own soul symbolizes itself completely in the action. Because the image Jean-Christophe is elemented by what in Rolland refuses to be imprisoned in the formula of patriotism, Jean-Christophe the character is permitted to be born in the Rhineland, and to come into France as a foreigner. He is clumsy, powerful, poor; for he is the movement of Rolland's heart dreaded of the French bourgeoise. Grazia, too, the Beatrice of the romance, the goal toward which the hero struggles, is a foreigner, an Italian. To Olivier, the over-sensitive plant reared in the hot-house of the French classical past, life comes in the guise of a rude music-making German. Music reconciles the incompatible fragments of the human soul. Music is the hero-saviour, setting life aflame.

And there is very little difference between "Jean-Christophe" and the position maintained by Rolland, the polemical work done by him, throughout the war. Both forms have made it possible for the world to know what the artist is. Both have tried to tear from the human heart the bands that separate it from the all. Both have carried against the hateful egoism of the war the sounding souls of the great lovers, held them up as in a monstrance and called men to memory of the human treasure. It may be Rolland did not know what was accompanying him in his steep ascent in Switzerland those dreadful long five years. Nevertheless, there was a presence leading him by the hand as the archangel once led Tobit. Long ago, music had taught him what it is to go in utter loneliness and still let no bitterness poison the full heart; to carry love of the world through a world which wanted to destroy that very love; to feel about one in the empty places the goodly host of the heroic dead. And now, it was placing his feet firm on a roadway which, through many years, under cover of the night, it had been building for them.

Were Beethoven to come alive to-day, it is probable he would wish he had never been born. He would find a multitude of people using something they called by his name in a spirit entirely opposed to his own. He would find himself dissipating life; he who had wished to give it greater abundance. He would meet a great many people who pretended to be thoroughly acquainted with him, among them, surely, "Théophile Goujat, the great musical critic, who . . . talked of sevenths and ninths"; and out of all these find scarcely a one having any grasp of his intentions. One sight there would be to greet his eyes, nevertheless, which might make him return thanks to heaven for his own career. And that would be Romain Rolland; not perhaps so much the art of Romain Rolland as his life. In that life, he would see something come into existence through himself, and evolved in his own spirit. One man, at least, among the men of the twentieth century, he would see, understood him. One man, at least, among the living, could show a world in what way art was to be used.

In that flash of knowledge he would have seen the kernel of all the moral grandeur which makes Rolland so precious to us.

January, 1917.

The End of the Kneisel Quartet

QUARTET ensembles have surpassed the Kneisel Quartet in beauty of execution. Kneisel himself was never the profound musician that Joachim was; that an half dozen of living leaders are. Something of dryness was always in his playing; and the tone of his partners, too, wanted the suavity and vibrancy which his own performance lacked. During the last years of the life of his organization, Willeke called from his 'cello a syrupy brilliance which was almost as trying as the scrapings heard on the strings of the first violin. Quartet ensembles have in recent years made known to the American public a euphony, a richness and delicacy of coloring which it never heard in the work of the Kneisels. Nevertheless, the Quartet of Franz Kneisel remains for us the excellent string-quartet. Such it must remain, for every one who heard it in the years of its vigor and effectiveness. No other body can become, it seems, more closely identified with the department of musical art this made its own; nor grow to shine more bravely with the very glory of quartet-music itself.

What it gave us, here in the United States, constitutes a portion of the national capital. If we have come to love string-quartet music; if cities the country over furnish audiences for work done in this medium, it is chiefly because of the whole-hearted, thirty-two-year-long labor done by Franz Kneisel and his associates. They came to us as part of the great influence bequeathed us by mid-European musical life. With Seidl, with Gericke, with the men and women who mounted Wagner's music drama, they deepened our taste and helped teach us to distinguish the artist from the charlatan. But of all the musicians who fertilized our soil, scarcely any accepted a more difficult task than did the Kneisels. Orchestral music, operatic music, both, are more facile of access than music for string ensembles is. The relative uniformity of the medium limits the range and character of the sonorities, and renders the distinctions subtle. The form demands in the composer who would essay it maturity and developed resourcefulness; it was by no chance that Haydn, Beethoven, and Franck expressed through it their most intimate and profound conceptions; and created through it the purest monuments of their arts. In the eighteenth century, the string-quartet was the plaything of courts and aristocratic societies; and the music written for it retained some of the delicacy and noble reserve of the situation which gave it birth. The romantics, attuned as they were to a more democratic public, nevertheless preserved in the music they wrote for it a like chastity. So serious, so severe has the medium remained that many excellent musicians have found it forbidding. Wagner, for instance, detested it. So too did Liszt. Usually magnificently catholic in his tastes, he called it, not "Kammermusik" but "Jammermusik." The American critic who not a long while since suggested that performances of it be relegated to musical "museums," could probably with ease have found other high authority for his contempt.

It is difficult for us whose eardrums they have refined to gauge how large a fund of courage and of selfless devotion these pioneers had to bring to their enterprise. String-quartet music has become a necessity to us; as great a one as orchestral and vocal and piano music concerts. And we are prone to forget there was a time the

form repelled us. It was indeed a desert Kneisel set out
to cross when he commenced his work. A desert it remained a long while. In the years first following its inception in Boston in 1885, his quartet played to tiny
audiences in New York City itself. In was long before it
drew large enough a house to fill even stuffy little Mendelssohn Hall. So weak was the demand for performances, that, until 1905 Kneisel found it possible to
remain concert master of the Boston Symphony Orchestra
as well as first violin of his own organization. So mani-
fold were the obstacles in his road that as late as 1907 he
thought seriously of abandoning his work and accepting
the financially more brilliant post of conductor of the
Philadelphia Orchestra. But the breaths of the prophets
were in him. He had a beauty to show. Life would
scarcely have been life could he not have shared his
treasure.

Over the East and center of the country he went, offering his beautiful concerts. Boston and New York were
never the only cities permitted to hear the Kneisels.
From the commencement of their existence, they traveled
outside the musical centers; perhaps for the reason that,
like Cæsar, they traveled light of musical baggage. They
went at first to near-by cities. Later, gradually, with
the years, they moved farther and farther west; going as
far as Chicago, covering each season a larger territory.
They went, ten, fifteen years ago, to towns which before
had rarely, almost never, heard the best of music properly
given; towns whose musical season was indeed "una per-
petua dormienda" broken only somewhat ineffectually by
concerts of college glee clubs, local ensembles, and, occasionally, by liedersinger. Possibly none other than those
who came to know the Kneisels in one of their assaults
upon a fortress of provincialism can fully appreciate the

nature and the quality of their patient toil, and the kind of gratitude due them. To the metropolitan audiences, their concerts, expeditions into undiscovered and wonderful land although they were, constituted merely a single element of a full and varied musical season. In the smaller towns, on the contrary, they gave the one musical experience. The wintry fog which lay sluggish upon the landscape was cut the evening you went for the first time in life up Market and down Main, past the lighted shops and the dark Opera House and the darker First Dutch Reformed or Second Congregational Church, to hear the Beethoven and Schubert and Brahms, in the Knights of Columbus Hall. For many minutes after you were seated, the evening seemed anything but tonic. The emptiness of the hall depressed; so, too, did the dinginess of the woodland or parlor scenery with which the small stage was set as though amateur theatricals were about to take place upon it. And when the four earnest men stepped on the stage with their fiddles; seated themselves before the lighted desks; placed their bows in position and, at the sudden nod of the leader commenced playing, the mood of the place did not at first brighten. The music was not at all, it was patent, like the "Pathétique" Symphony when Saffanoff conducted it; or like Tannhäuser's hymn to Venus in the opera. In was hard to follow, and rather dark brown. You kept falling into vacant trances, and waking up to find that you had forgotten you were assisting at a concert.

Nevertheless, by the time the first intermission arrived, something had happened. You were in the state of one who had been looking despondently over waste land, and had suddenly seen gush here and there from the caked mould little crystal rills. They had gushed momentarily only. But the moments had followed each other at short intervals. By the time of the second intermission, you had seen in spite of a growing sleepiness, more waters, laughing brooks, gleaming pools, waters not colorless only but green and blue and silver too. And then, the poverty of the house began to exasperate. Those men had lost money coming to this cursed burg! They could hardly pay for the hall! Never would they return; and now forever would one be left to the untender mercies of the Amherst College Glee Club singing "Juanita" and "Lord Geoffrey Amherst was a Soldier of the King." Hence, when the instrumentalists returned to the stage to give the last number, you applauded resonantly in the hope that the hearty welcome might atone for the scant attendance. And next day it was pleasant to hear that the local music dealer was thinking of getting together a guarantee fund for the purpose of bringing the Kneisels back again next year.

It must have been the inwardness with which they played that persuaded so promptly, and held their audiences, metropolitan and provincial, in a sort of abstract grasp whilst yet the music they were giving remained bewildering and half-shut. Genuineness has a fair way of throwing bridges through the perilous air; and their performances had always the generosity of conception, the conscientiousness of workmanship natural to musicians who live through their art. Nor was the standard of execution maintained through a restriction of the range of their repertory. Quartet music was touched in Bach and in Ravel and Kodály and Enesco; and of the individual expressions which lay between these temporal poles, very few were overlooked. Lighter talents, such as those of Tchaikowsky, Smetana and Dvorák, figured on their programs. But the body of their concerts consisted invariably of the performance of works by the classic

masters, Haydn and Mozart, Beethoven and Brahms. A
good number of mixed forms were included, piano quar-
tets and quintets; and from time to time additional
players of stringed instruments were introduced into the
major system of the four for the performance of sextets
and septets. To be sure, it was apparent, before the
Kneisels disbanded, that they were fast approaching the
physical limits assigned by personality to their perceptivi-
ties. The little diatonic folk-song tune in the last movement of the second Kodály quartet, was most evidently to
them a city of refuge in which they might gratefully repose themselves after the ardors of their chase through
the more dissonant, free and pungent preceding movements. Still, out of a sense of responsibility toward the
musical public, or because of a genuine intellectual curiosity, they persisted to the very time of the dissolution of
their partnership in pushing outward the boundaries of
their repertory; one of their last discoveries was "Verklärte Nacht" by Schoenberg.

And in the end of the organization, there expressed
itself the selfsame honest love of quality which gave it
birth and maintained it in existence so long. Aware that
he could no longer manage to hold his quartet quite to the
high standard conceived by him in former years; unwill-
ing to permit it to become the shadow of what he wanted
it to be, Franz Kneisel in the spring of 1917 disbanded
"the Kneisels."

We remain indebted to them to-day no less than during
the time they still used to come onto the platform of
Æolian Hall and, seating themselves in the shape of an
introverted square, strike their fiddle-strings. They have
entered the soil of America as vitalizers. The great Germanic influence of which they were part lies rich upon the
hardpan of our colonial culture. The earnestness and

the wholesomeness of the elder German musical life still
lives on in our concert halls, in the very thick of the stuffy
air. For, provincial and precociously weary as we are,
we remain, unlike lively France, used to technically accomplished and carefully prepared performances.

Where audiences appear specially for the purpose of
hearing quartet music played, there the Kneisels remain,
invisible, and still at work. And, if ever a chamber music
with "physiognomy characteristic and western" comes to
grow in America, it will carry these men in some degree in
trunk and branch and twig, as the tree carries, the virtue
of the earth in which it stands planted. It may be no such
art will ever be given us. It may be we cannot transform
into power the contribution made us by these musicians;
and that we shall ever remain a barbarous people. If we
so remain, it will be through no deed of theirs. They
gave us the best that men can give each other. They
gave us a chance.

February, 1917.

Patriotic Concert

THE first war months had the quality of the slow minutes which, in time of sickness, withdraw the cloud-curtains of sleep and lay bare consciousness of anguish. They were the tearing fierce minutes become endless. In coma, you had dreamt yourself independent of the power which was loudest, most vibrant and masterful in the towers and gulches of lower Manhattan. Between the visible temporal power and your very inner self, it had seemed, there was no real connection. You had assumed yourself unsubjected of any worldly might, a single and inviolable entity. Skin was an armor excluding all. That no friendliness at all stretched between you and the presence which found its chief exercise-place among these stones, that had been plain. You had found its way and works ugly and monstrous and dull. And it, in turn, you were assured, considered you utterly without usefulness. Nevertheless, a sense of being disregarded quite and free to go your eccentric way had dreamt itself in your brain. The cloth of convention was on your back. And, by means of this external observance, it had seemed, you had placed the living portion of you entirely beyond the reach of the pinnacles of steel.

But of a sudden a pretense of protection extended over you had collapsed. The old party who had been standing at the corner playing every one's benevolent uncle; posing as a paternal traffic policeman who convoyed school children at the street crossing; arresting with Roman white-gloved hand motor trucks and horse drays that the inno-

27

cents might pass before them safe as the Israelites in the
Red Sea, had with terrible effortlessness wiped the benevolence from off his countenance. He had not, as he did it,
turned squarely to face you. With a bare brutal look of
businesslikeness he had jerked his stiffened thumb four or
five times over his shoulder youward. And this elegant
gesture had indicated you to a person in vizor and khaki
who but a moment since you had considered merely an
imbecile charitably indulged by the kindly old party in
an apparently harmless passion for chest protrusion on all
occasions and for hieratic solemn self-exhibition to brass
music; but who now with perfect mechanical readiness
took drover-like possession of the baggage turned over to
him. Finished was the comedy of benevolence. Formerly,
they had gone around the country with press gangs shang-
haiing yokels. Now, they did it swifter by law. You
roused from sleep to find claws dug in your shoulder flesh.
Popped into nothingness like a soap-bubble was the imagined inviolacy. You were trapped. You were in the
black shadows of the skyscrapers; held amid the masonry
of this raw city world as in a jail; chained to its lumbering
chariot and about to be dragged to Gehenna in its wake.

Insolent hands were reaching out toward the quick and
secret part of you. Insolent hands for the first time were
intruding upon your privacy and seizing hold of the essential sensitive substance. Always it had stood alone, the
vital part of you; looking elsewhere than the region occupied by the skyscrapers; looking into the distances smoky
and mauve as the afternoon sky over the iron and chimneys and houselets of the Jersey bluffs. Always, it had
been engaged in its stilly secret play of little shooting
arrows light and winged and incalculable as the tiny
darts shot through the blowgun of a Malayan brave;
shy, tiny vagrant arrows that came now singly, now not

at all, now thick upon each other in squadrons; and found
an unpremeditated surprising way into the fecund dark
quick of life; discovering now a new object; gaining now
a new wisdom; opening now a fresh vista; inventing now
a novel pleasure; forming now a new jewel. And, in the
war crisis, this vital you had turned disdainfully from the
broil, knowing it for a weak miserable misdeed. It could
not be drugged and deceived. It knew it worthless, all,
and unimportant to the man-spirit. It knew the broil of
infinitely less consequence to the man-spirit than its own
proper play of silent vagrant pointed arrows penetrating
unpredictably into the dark tissue of the world.

And yet, it was not the draft alone that warred upon
the self. Indeed, the draft, which at one time seemed to
be driving a dividing wedge into the very entrails of the
self, and be menacing the citadel of the spirit, in truth
penetrated no farther than the suburbs of the city.
Another act, or set of actions, penetrated farther into
sacred territory, and crushed areas of an unknown sensitivity underneath their hoofs.

To a single individual, at the very least, the nature and
violence of these acts became finally apparent through
nothing seemingly more relevant than a concert. The
performance, in the course of which this one mind felt the
last rending of the cloud-curtains, was the first of the
series of concerts given in the summer of 1917 by the
hastily organized Civic Orchestral Society under the
leadership of Pierre Monteux, then fresh from Paris.

It was folly to have attended such a concert. Nothing
other than extreme depression could have resulted. The
entire series of which it formed part was advertised as
Patriotic. And in those days angels themselves dared
scarcely tread at entertainments not specifically so labeled.
One could assist at scarce a musical show, a concert

or a movie, without encountering some form of wartime
vulgarity. But as the man of whom I speak had not as
yet completely awakened to the ugliness of the situation,
he went.

And, at the commencement of the evening, it seemed to
him as though merely the customary ritual of Patriotism
was in process. St. Nicholas Rink, the scene of the performance, was draped of course with the stars and stripes,
the union jack and the tricouleur, and looked exactly like
the building at county fairs in which they exhibit cake
and pickles. Two verses of "The Star-spangled Banner"
were sung by Anna Case of the Opera gracefully draped in
the folds of the national banner. One took it that the
army was immediately fired to unusual heroism. M.
Monteux conducted the overture to "Le Roi d'Ys," the
symphonic interlude of Franck's "Redemption," and the
familiar air from "Louise." He conducted them well.
The third "Leonore" overture he conducted badly; and
the piece of Bach's with which he prefaced the concert
contained some surprising strands of counterpoint probably not by the composer. Nature, it seemed, was taking
her course. It was only when, at the close of the intermission, Monteux did not reappear on the platform, and
a little banker accompanied by an army officer in regalia,
appeared in his place, that the alarm bell within began
violently to toll. It was apparent, too late, that no man
might venture into a patriotic concert and hope unscathed
to go.

The little banker made a speech. Just what the little
banker intended to signify by his speech was not at first
easily to be perceived. He began by congratulating the
audience on the fact that art was still neutral, and then
expressed his extreme gratification that the conductor of
the concerts of the Civic Orchestral Society was a "son

of France." (No one who was not present can imagine
with what unction and sonority the little banker pro-
nounced the word "France." 'Tis an ill wind indeed which
blows no good; and, in a way, it was worth going to have
heard it.) He further registered his delight that the
realm of music had not as yet been contaminated by the
war, and announced that it was the intention of the Civic
Orchestral Society, of which he was treasurer, to demon-
strate the connection between music and patriotism by
introducing into the course of each of the concerts
speeches on Patriotism and Art and allied subjects. Having arrived by these zigzags at what finally revealed itself
the point of his address: the introduction of the personage
in uniform, Colonel Somebody, U. S. A., the little banker
descended from the rostrum and left the Colonel to make
his address on Art and Patriotism and other allied subjects.

The Colonel's ideas on Art and Patriotism were sol-
dierly and Allied in the extreme. He reminded the audience that volunteering in New York City was lagging;
that only a fraction of the quota had offered itself for
service. He was positive that every one in the audience
who was not himself fit for service knew some young man
who was; and could bring pressure to bear on him. He
could not recommend sufficiently the benefits to be de-
rived from joining the army. It made, he said, all the
good in you "come out." Because of the wages paid the
soldiers, the army to-day compared favorably with all
other professions. In fact, simply because of the educa-
tional advantages it offered you, no other institution could
rival it. And, best of all, those who joined the army
Made the World Safe for Democracy, and enabled their
Country to have at its Disposal, after the war was over, a
Large Body of Trained Men.

Many other pearls of purest Platonism dropped from the colonel's mouth. Finally, through a sort of dizzy mist one saw a pair of black coat tails dust the platform of the conductor's stand, and realized that the colonel had finished; that Monteux was once more preparing to start the music; and that it had become Beethoven's turn to drum up recruits.

During that half-hour's recruiting, the drafted man of whom I have spoken sank into blacks he had not known the world could contain. Scarce had the vulgar exhibition of the muddled little banker and the professional soldier begun before he knew the most fundamental right of his being no longer existed. He had been abolished. He was still sitting in the chair. But as an independent being he had been wiped out as a sum is wiped from a schoolboy's slate. The arms and legs had been lopped from off him. They had been cut off close at pit and groin; and he was no more than a helpless stump impotent to move himself an inch. They had been rent from him as coolly as though they, his necessary implements, were the toys with which a child amused himself, and which could be snatched away arbitrarily by an impatient elder, without excuse. He had been robbed of what was most important to him. The impudent robbers absolved themselves completely of any guilt; and he could find no power able to interfere in his behalf and help him protest his rights.

Conscription had only partially invaded his rights. The sort of thought-dragooning of which the speechifying in the Rink was typical, assaulted him in a more criminal fashion. It assaulted life as a whole. The draft had attacked life in portion only. It threatened to interfere with a portion of the community only. But the violation of thought struck at all men. It assaulted the spirit as spirit. There can be no life at all and no men where there

is no right of man to the privacy of his own inner chamber.
There can be nothing but machines where there is no
right of man to the inviolacy of his relationship with himself. It is in the silence, the privacy of that place that he
hears the sovereign voice. It is within the six walls that
he stands on holy ground. It is in prayer; it is in vigil;
it is in contemplation; it is in all the acts of hearing and
seeing and uttering that fill the cavern with sound and
light that man has learned the ground-song of his being,
and come to know what he knows. And that ground-
song they were determined to drown.

So this was the way, then, in which it came, the Inquisi-
tion! It made no long slow approach. It did not have to
give fair warning a great way off, like a locomotive.
There was no law prescribing it manners. It might meet
you in any secluded country road, and crush you there.
The young man who felt himself completely under the
wheels that night had been educated in such a way that
the grim impasses of life had been to him something
proper like doublets and ruffs to dark-gone centuries;
something which could no more breathe in this time of
light than slaves in England. The situation in which men
had found themselves when they had to choose between
everything that was holy to them and the rack and the
stake; the sort of arbitrary power which descended upon
people and sent them to freeze in the salt mines of Siberia,
had seemed as remote from him in time as Bloody Mary,
and as far removed in space as St. Petersburg. But here
in the midst of modern conveniences, electric-lit America,
it had fronted him, a bowlder suddenly fallen out of the
clouds above his head right before his feet. It had come
to him through persons whose fathers were supposed to
have suffered and bled at the hands of violators of conscience, and to have called this power abominable tyranny,

and revolted from it. Now their sons with mouths full of
the praise of dead soldiers of liberty were themselves
become the oppressors; and gave themselves the style of
heroes. They did not see the falsehood. They did not
see that between them and the German there was no
difference.

Still, the situation was not the same as it was in the
dark past. Then, men did not take everything lying down.
They fought, then; they resisted the king and priests;
they threw down the glove of the body and let the worldly
powers have their glut of it. But here, no one opposed.
The people in St. Nicholas Rink that evening felt that the
interference with the performance, the ceremony, of
music, which had been perpetrated upon them wasn't bad;
but worse than bad; vulgar. American audiences signify
their disapproval in remaining silent, whether from dislike
of publicity or from timidity one does not know. And
this one remained silent. People listened to the speeches
with heads bent over their laps; with disdainfully smiling
faces; and whispered remarks not sympathetic to the
speakers. And yet, no one protested. No one arose to
tell the financier that what he was perpetrating was a
contemptibly vulgar thing. No one arose in all the country to stop the dragooning of thought. Something had
altered in life; something had gone soft and decayed in
stamina. These people, the heirs of agelong fights for
freedom of conscience, of fights for the rights of individuals to be safe in their persons and in their beliefs, did
not, could not, would not raise a hand in defense of their
hardwon privileges. Perhaps the odds were greater
against the revolté now than then. Whatever it was, the
old spirit of fight was gone out of these frames. The
young drafted man knew it in himself. His arms were
limp. He was alone. He felt himself alone. The few men

here and there in the country who were going to protest; to see it through and take their medicine were not enough for him. He couldn't feel them about him. The other power with its skyscrapers was about him. He could have gotten up and gone out. The law of the skyscraper people said that he could leave the hall if he wanted. They probably wouldn't have hung him to a lamp-post for doing so. The judge would certainly not have sentenced him to prison had they arrested him. No more than a few disdaining regards; no more than a hiss or two, would have met him. Perhaps nothing at all. But he did not get up and go. He sat and let them do it.

July, 1917.

Palestrina on Twenty-second Street

YOUR banal American will sing. He will sing not only on hay-rides and on the steps of fraternity houses. He will sing for the very sake of song. That, has been demonstrated by the progress of the Community Chorus movement. Before it began, the most of us were sure the New World had produced a sort of passive man who did not need to express himself as the men in the Old had done, ever, and was content to pay others to perform for him. In America you could not, as you could in so many districts of Europe, go through the streets of little cities at nightfall and hear from taverns and dwellings the sound, like to lighted Christmas trees, of people chanting musically together. Only the darkey sang. The white man worked and berayed with his mouth. The living and cherished folk-singing, the function which had been the solace and refreshment of laboring races, and made possible musical art, seemed to have vanished quite. It too, apparently, had been killed in transit to new conditions.

Then, splendid refutation, came the Community Chorus movement. One had but to assist at a single of its assemblages in park or schoolhouse or hippodrome to recognize that not everything had been lost. One had but to observe the faces of those gathered at one of the "festivals" to gauge to what a degree the old creative lust smoldered on. They were the faces of those who, we had been told, had been tired completely by a life of misuse, and had lost all desire to make beautiful things. And yet, as the singing rose and spread and grew, and gathered up and made

36

one those thousands of people, there came over faces an incandescence, a liberation that was like the cracking of age-old glaciers.

This discovery has been the chief effect of the Community Chorus movement. In itself, no doubt, it is a considerable achievement. But it is an insufficient one. Only the production of the popular musical impulse in worthy form would have been a quite satisfactory achievement, and it is precisely that which the Community Chorus has not succeeded in effecting. For it has not found a matter through which its gatherings could express themselves really. We have, of course, little American folk-music of any great value. There exist, no doubt, some very beautiful negro spirituals. But the very conditions that have prevented us from singing have prevented us as well from getting a genuine popular art. Popular American music is represented, at best, by Stephen Foster's songs, and for the greater part by concoctions stereotyped either in rhythm or in melody, stereotyped always in harmony, and generally in all three.

And the leaders of the Community Chorus movement have shown little ability to satisfy this want. They have, it is true, urged all the American composers to write them songs, and have at times attempted to teach their congregations classical music. But, on the whole, they have shown quite as great a tendency to permit themselves to be led by their helpless gatherings as to lead. And so we find them assembling thousands of people for the purpose of singing "Old Black Joe." That, in itself, is a procedure of questionable value. But of the value of assembling thousands of people for the purpose of singing "Silver Threads Among the Gold" there can be no question. Latterly, the gatherings appeared to have been brought about for the business of teaching the public the words of "Over There" and other patriotic compositions. And when attempts have been made to lead the assemblages, the result, like the bawling of choruses from "The Messiah" and "The Creation" that was to be heard at some of the "festivals," has been thoroughly unmusical. One comes away from so many of the Community Chorus meetings glad, indeed, that a general need of singing does exist, but deeply disappointed that it has been satisfied only in such trivial form.

About the time of war's ending, however, there came into being an instrument capable of producing the lyrical impulse worthily. This, was the chorus formed by the People's Music League of the People's Institute of New York for the purpose of studying the polyphonic works of the fifteenth and sixteenth centuries. It may not have been a deeper reverence for the impulse pent in folk that initiated this effort. Certainly a very sincere reverence initiated the Community Chorus movement. But it indubitably was a keener sense of the problem that moved this newcomer. The end of both enterprises, of course, was the release of creative power, the generation of a direct, genuine, and fluent gift of expression that will find America its musical idiom, and so continue to enrich national life. The persons responsible for the newer, however, seem to have recognized beforehand that the singing of "Old Black Joe" and "Silver Threads Among the Gold" could not give folk any true release, and that what was required to make community singing successful was a musical experience that would draw out and unfold the powers of the singers. It was unfortunate, no doubt, that such an unfolding could not be gotten through the music with which the general public was familiar. Nevertheless there was a body of music that would afford it. This was the polyphonic vocal art of the Renaissance.

The work of the giants of that time has never been excelled in delicacy and freedom. Josquin des Pres is no less limpid and sweet of heart than Mozart; Vittoria the Spaniard no less sultry-sensuous than Chopin; Orlando di Lasso no less awesome than Bach. Perhaps their musics are even more proper to our own day than those of the men of the last two centuries. We have been struggling toward an unconfinement in rhythmic beat and in thematic structure which they possessed more largely than it has ever since been had of any one. Their beat was not limited by regularly recurrent bar-lines, nor their structure by hard patterns and chromatic formulæ. In small space, through the subtlety and irregularity and clarity of their form, they achieved a sense of immeasurable size. Modern music goes upward towards nature and the polyphonic men.

True, this richest legacy of the musical past reveals itself in all its beauty only to those possessing patience and zest for study. But, for the men and women who planned the "People's Chorus," the patient study of music for the sake of learning was one of the few forms of action worthy of the impulse that existed in people about them. Given a conductor who could manipulate such machinery, and teach people to sing Palestrina and Vittoria, and one group, they knew, would safely be afoot.

In M. Ernest Bloch the directors found the conductor wanted. Apart even from his magnificent creative power, M. Bloch is an exception among musicians. He belongs neither to the large class of those, who, like Mr. Kurt Schindler, for example, have a remarkable intellectual grasp of their métier and are nevertheless incapable of incorporating living warmth in a performance; nor to the equally large class of those who like Mr. Ossip Gabrilowitch possess an exquisite gift of interpretation, but want catholicity of taste. He belongs to the very small company of musicians who are both fertile and thoroughly acquainted with the history and master works of their art. And he possesses the perfect liberality of imagination, the perfect independence of routine, the good sportsmanship and real artistry necessary to the success of the enterprise. For the manner of procedure projected for the chorus was unconventional completely. No idea of "performance" was connected with it. The weekly meetings were not intended as rehearsals for some ultimate concert in Carnegie Hall, with choristers in pink silks and boiled shirtfronts. They were intended ends in themselves. The singing was to be done entirely for its own sake; entirely for the pleasure of it. Every Monday evening at eight the auditorium of the Manhattan Trade School on Twenty-second Street was to be open to everybody, to all those without distinctions of race, creed, color, or previous condition of servitude who wished to come and study the old polyphonic music. There was to be two hours of work. That was all.

With what fresh green did one not watch the inception of the new movement! It was the end of the war; and, even then, one had not as yet been cured entirely. The People were still to be found, so the mists still seductively wavered, just without the door. To be sure, the army had done greatly to disabuse of the dream. One had gone forward religiously to meet the American man, strong, generous, and free, and one had found nothing save unclarity. In certain, a very thin sheet of clear water extended atop the mud. In a few isolated creatures, immigrants mostly, it even extended downward an inch or two. Sooner or later, however, and generally immediately, one had struck the mud. But it was obvious these poor bags of things had been met under conditions certain to produce to the full whatever the human breast contained of meanness. And by Humanity one had never meant the young man. Humanity only commenced with the mature man, the man who had had a few children, and worked hard for his family. Humanity was everybody who never held a position of power, and who lived something in itself too large to become evident. Above all, Humanity was women. Yes, it was of women something in one was thinking of when one innocently said, "I believe in People." Them, also, one had seen in the war; and with amaze. But this vision had been received only as some poor travesty of woman conjured up by the imbecile male. She was not like this in herself. This, was the fruit of subjection. A seed was brooding in darkness removed entirely of the institutions made by man. Some day it would sprout and come into the world like the girl in "The Master-Builder" . . . all pine woods and rivulets under snow and mountain inviolacy.

For sight of this fineness, then, which institutions would not let be and governments perverted, one waited, the table spread. Sometimes, to be sure, the vigil seemed foolhardy. Palestrina, Josquin des Pres, Orlando di Lasso, those shadowy dim musicians on Twenty-second Street, New York! The two ideas seemed irreconcilable. One had been made to associate these delicate masters with "concerts of old music" and special occasions removed far from the roar. Still, the old bells rang forth. No great technical obstacle prevented the teaching of such musics to a band of amateurs. The possession of a little voice and the capacity to read one's part rendered the works accessible to any one eager to participate. And the People, one knew, were just outside the door. The fine clear thing in them had been insulted by Cooper Union alms; this opening at the Manhattan Trade School

was the sweetest invitation to the suppressed fineness.
Perhaps no more than a couple of hundred would regularly assist. But that would not matter really. Even
a couple of hundred faithful souls would be able to give
one sight of the view one wanted above all others.

Well, the lesson of the war was to be learned nowhere
better than in the Trade School during the sessions of
that unfortunate chorus! Your banal American will sing,
it is true. He will sing not only on hay-rides and on the
steps of fraternity houses, but for the very sake of song.
Nevertheless, the degree of intensity which transforms
the banal outflow into a thing of quality is not in him.
There was nothing excessively steep in the opportunity
offered by the People's Music League. There was no real
unrelatedness between music and singers. During the
very first session, the senselessness of making com-
promises and trying to "go down" to the public was demonstrated. The folk who composed the little gathering
were not any different sort from those who sang "My
Old Kentucky Home" at the assemblages of the Community Chorus. And there was something in them perfectly ready for the classics. M. Bloch did not have
to sit long at the piano and explain the motets that had
been selected for performance. Within the hour, one of
those Aves of Josquin's that are like to some sweet serene
luminous fresco of Fra Angelico, and a motet of Pier-
luigi's, were sung. The singing was rude, the voices
uncertain. But the art of music was functioning again;
so much so, that one found oneself croaking along one's
own small bit.

And yet, the first group, comprising between forty and
fifty souls, was the vastest of all assembled by the chorus.
It seemed vaster and vaster as time progressed. Every
one had fervently promised to bring his friends and spread

the glad tidings and be punctual until death. And every
one had meant it when he swore. But the season is very
brilliant in New York, full of most tempting turns and
movies. And more and more people did not return. The
grandest musics came out of M. Bloch's brief-case;
musics above Bach and beyond Beethoven. Soon, however, the chorus formed by the People's Music League of
the People's Institute of New York became a thing really
pitiful to look at. A few faithful men who looked like
superannuated clerks. A few pinched and meagre
women; school teachers, probably. Once, from a motor,
several excessively swathed ladies descended, and were
given copies of Orlando and Vittoria to sing. But they
very obviously found the sixteenth century masterpieces
not at all what they had been led to expect. They had
anticipated, it seemed, a social function and Mrs. Somebody. They never appeared again. Soon, the foremost
musician in America was left exhorting a dozen or fourteen persons. One carried off the memory of a marvelous
absorption on the platform, of a man hearing golden
alleluias and seraphs' hymnings; pleading, explaining,
cajoling; and not being able to believe the mystic caroll-
ings not every tittle as present and luminous to other
ears as to his own. And, in a few of the seats beneath his
tense-strained body, a haggard handful of folk.

Some say there are no People; that what makes a noise
and walks on Broadway and Fifth Avenue, and on Second Avenue, too, is in reality the completest of illusions;
and that you have but to reach out your hand and try to
lay hold on solid to find how utterly unsubstantial it is.
There is nothing there, they say, merely a hollow show
born of the diseased brain. One does not know whether
this particular song is too early or too late. Certainly,
none of the persons who saw the comic disaster of Pales-

trina on Twenty-second Street were found singing it.
Twelve or fourteen individuals are a great many, as things
go; and a few times a year one finds oneself timidly adding
to the number after seeing here a face, there the proud
twitch of a plain cloak, there the free carriage of a figure
standing up to dance. Surely, if these come, there must be
more. There are a few rooms, also. Nevertheless, a vari-
ant of the terrible tune must have been reverberated in
every breast. What not the war, and not even the Peace,
had succeeded in driving home, that, a few glimpses of an
empty schoolroom had carried. The doorsill was vacant.
The fine general thing for which all fine deeds are done,
and toward which they send their call, was not in sight.
The street, as far as the corner, was bare. Round the
corner, there might be something. But one could not
be sure.

March, 1919.

D'Indy

D'INDY's music has the high grace of quality. It expresses a spirit perhaps neither very powerful nor fecund, but distinguished and upright and noble in essence. In all its parts, it gives again the fine cool breath of a dignified and fundamentally lofty nature. Manner not a whit less than matter is impregnated with it. What he has to bring, D'Indy offers us in nobly chased vessels. The compositions of no living musician, not Ravel's even, come fashioned with greater richness and dexterity and purity of workmanship, than come those of the mature D'Indy. Their exquisite subtlety and firmness of detail, their hardness and precision and fulness, make them appear a little like pieces of superb goldsmithery executed in the fluid medium of tone; platters and basins and cups of precious metal whose simple perfection of line is accented rather than destroyed by the reliefs of fruit and leaf and flower fantasy graven upon them. The b-flat symphony, the pianoforte sonata, the sonata for violin and piano, are complex and solid edifices built up of many cunningly and brilliantly and firmly carven periods of sound. Over every shape found by D'Indy's sensuous French nature in the medium of orchestra or piano; over every bit of music, over bits most minor to his scheme no less than over passages the most major, an infinitely patient and sensitive hand has passed; passed innumerable times, it would seem; intensely, passionately refining. Tender modulation dissolves in tender modulation. Every movement, every fragment of theme, every strand of counterpoint,

45

has been brought to sharpest life. The inner movement has been preserved in every note of the structure. And in the matter which murmurs and bursts and flares from the instruments, we feel with delight always the sharpness of the chaser's tools; the edges and surfaces of the steely blades and hammers that chiselled and beat till the subject metal became the great scintillant complex of points of light.

And what the dish contains most oftentimes has a gravity and a largeness worthy of the ceremoniousness with which it is presented. D'Indy's power is no *kleinmeisterei;* no application of exquisite scruples to trifles of art. His major works, the b-flat symphony, the poem of the mountain, the sonatas, are generously conceived. They are spacious moving things; long lines which circle and spiral in ample sweeps, and terminate in majestic chorale-like proclamations of the germinal ideas. The composer is one of the few Frenchmen of the generation subsequent to that of Franck and Saint-Saëns and Lalo who have found themselves in the larger and more complicated and severe forms. He was born a symphonist; born armed with the lungpower necessary to the management of great involuted structures of tone, and necessary to the production of ideas proportionate to them. The introductory motif of the sonata Op. 63, with its rude hollow octaves and fourths, heaves on with an almost Beethoven-like broadness and furor; the black clangor of the instrument places us immediately in the heroic lands where move the male sonatas of the master of B̄onn. The themes of the final movement of this work; the theme of the finale of his work for violin, burst forth in all the magnificence of great sweeping gestures; and, despite the almost excessive richness of their harmonic vesture, their well-nigh Wagnerian pomp, move with the

freshness of springtime lyricism. Others speak with a
great quiet dignity; with a grave melancholy; a tenderness which remains always austere and sober. The trio of
the violin sonata is like the voice of some one speaking
gravely and in serene passionateness. If D'Indy has not
become an important inventor of idiom; if much of his
material remains always to a certain degree derivative
from Franck and from Wagner, some individual twist of
austerity and angularity, some harmonic refinement almost invariably informs his themes with his own aristocratic temper. Herzeleide's grief, and the sad horn theme
of the last act of "Tristan," may echo through the final
movements of the violin sonata. The desert of "Parsifal," the snarling fire-magic of Logi, may glimmer
through the great work for piano. Franckishly shaped and
Franckishly disposed themes may appear in all D'Indy's
essays in symphonic form. Nevertheless, the elegance
and acerbity of D'Indy's harmonies, the sudden irruptions
of ninths and elevenths and whole-tone progressions; the
strange and individual sensuousness of his orchestra, with
its cutting, hard-edged brass, its acrid and medicinal
woodwind, its metallic scintillance, transmutes the Wagnerian ideas, and the Flemish broadness of Franck into
something shaped on D'Indy's own racial substance and
individual principle.

Shoddy work, pretentious work, vulgar work, D'Indy
cannot do; has never been able to do. The care, the
labor, the high seriousness which he has brought to his
composition, and expended upon it, are spontaneous and
necessary expressions of his being. D'Indy's failures
flow from the states of drouth which overtake him oftentimes; not from any cheapness of spirit or slovenliness of
conception. Despite the narrowness of outlook, the grotesque theorizing, the occasional outbursts of ugliness

which characterize some of his verbal utterances, he is
fundamentally a creature in whom fineness is perfectly
housed. He is indeed the fine French gentleman; the
Frenchman whose innate nobility has made him to take
up into himself something of the largeness and dignity of
spirit left in the world about him by his forebears; and to
give it new and individual form in the essential expressions of his life. Within this austere old man there must
breathe something which is like the instinct of women
who, without any priggishness, without any self-complacency and egoism, but because of an inflexible impera-
tive within them, preserve themselves for the creatures
of their own plane. This musician, too, it seems, has some
inner and half-conscious relation to the universe because
of which he has been unable to live life, to meet any of
its manifestations, whether in the shape of human beings
or musical instruments or sheets of blank score paper,
save in the spirit of high decency and respectfulness.
Reverence for the stuff within his own breast, because it
is a real awe, has become in him a reverence for all things:
for men and trees and mountains, for musicians dead and
musicians living. He has been unable, when he has come
to his worktable, not to desire to give himself with all
the largeness and sweetness and disinteredness of spirit
of which he is capable; not to desire to record what of
purity and wonderfulness he has encountered. The impulse to make things easy for himself, to treat his conceptions in a spirit of insolent self-complacency and brutal
indifference to the men and women to whom he was offering it, to produce flimsy and pretentious work, if it has
come to him, must have come to him with the loathsome
look of an impulse to degrade into the mire the human
image within his own breast. And he has fled it all his
days as death-in-life.

And, being a person of quality, he has found himself
stronger than the torn, destructive vulgar Paris round
about him. The fashions of the musical world, minor
poetry and its petty politics have not been able to eat at
all into his large feeling for life. Showy and cheap music
has taken the road before his. The crowd of critics has
shouted its hosannahs in the wake of many a genius and
impostor since he began his labors. His compositions
have never met with popular favor. Musicians whom he
has respected, Debussy among them, have declared, many
times over, the symphony a form utterly alien to the
French temperament, and recommended their compatriots
to other forms. D'Indy, however, has not lost confidence
in the promptings of his own heart; or ceased from struggling in behalf of the French symphonic school; or loos-
ened his own severe and subtle and unpopular style. An
arm seems always to have been in him upholding the
inner roof; a voice laughing that what folk said about his
work, or did out in the streets of Paris, in no way affected
its value. A sense as strong as his of what the great men,
his masters, carried about with them in their proud and
lonely hearts, could not but have banished little personal
woes. A sort of priestly consecration to his own vision of
life seems early to have come over him, making him to go
his own solitary way proudly and indifferently. From
the beginning of his career he has stood always upon the
unpopular side. He was a friend and devoted disciple of
Franck while the old man was still little more than an
obscure organist, despised and disliked by musicians and
utterly unknown to officialdom; and all through his life
he has been fighting with a wondrous love and enthusiasm,
for the Belgian's mystical and tender art. With Bordès
and Guilmant he founded the Schola Cantorum, the musical school devoted to winning the uprising generations of

musicians to the purest vision of musical art, and to
spreading a high and unpopular musical culture. He has
constituted himself editor of Monteverde; managed even
to secure performance for "L'Incoronazione di Poppea."
The world about him has been mad and drunken and
falling. He has been standing with the rest of mankind
upon the deck of a foundering ship, ignorant whether it
is the next minute or the next hour that is to see the giant
paw of the ocean sweep everything under. But the fact
that the next minute may be his last in life has not
apparently made him to alter his conduct. He is still the
honest composer, the devoted teacher. An old man, he
comes to his *bureau* daily, regularly, to meet his pupils,
to make his criticisms, to fight for the human soul as
though the world were a pathway of gold into the sun.
No priestly consecration could be more complete than his.

Because of this informing spirit, D'Indy's music seems
destined very little less certainly than any other produced
during our hour, to long survival. Into the premier rank
of musicians its author will, of course, not go; for the
reason that he is not a robust, a released and abundant
nature. The great free air of the elements is not in his
art. If portions of it do have the fresh acrid aroma smelling of his native Cevennes and of warmth underneath the
summer pines, others breathe the stuffy air of the enclosed room, and smell of the lamp. If the b-flat symphony and the sonatas and "Un jour d'été sur la mon-
tagne" are indeed grave and moving hymns to life, they
stand as such somewhat apart in a body of work generally
a little thin and awkward and Calvinistic; and they, even,
suffer from the constriction of the composer's nature.
The clumsy scherzo of the Op. 63 weakens what is almost
the most beautiful piano sonata written. The opening
phrase of the sonata for violin, exalted and rich as it is,

irritates because of the slavery to a rhythm into which
D'Indy fell while composing it. Even the b-flat symphony
is marred by occasional passages of rhetoric unworthy of
the chaste nobility of the work. While D'Indy remains in
contemplative and Wordsworthian mood, he remains persuasive and colorful. But in other moods, he is less im-
pressive. There are many regions of life of which he
knows nothing. The music given to "La reine de
volupté" in the "Légende de St. Christophe" is banal and
almost absurd, and recalls nothing so much as the bourgeois enchantments of Vivianne in Goldmark's "Merlin."
Poor D'Indy can no more represent this rhythm of life
than Franck, his master, could represent the spirit of
evil in the Beatitudes.

Too many of his works seem to have commenced in
him not as sensuous perceptions, but as pure ideas. The
fleshing process has come as a secondary and independent movement. Of such an erratic proceeding, the
"Istar" variations have always seemed to us the result.
For the unhappy form, the declaration of the theme only
subsequent to the statement of the variations, has remained always somewhat irritating to us and wanting in
inner necessity. Certainly, it is his unfortunate propensity to theorize in the clouds where he ought to be studying the hard earth, which has limited the scope of
D'Indy's teaching. Many French and vulgar prejudices
have prevented him from giving his pupils a broad and
free interpretation of musical art. Romain Rolland has
compared the Schola Cantorum to a window giving not
upon the open, but upon a courtyard. It is true that
an odor of dankness and devout old lady pervades the
spiritual atmosphere of the institution, and makes it only
half healthy to the lungs. It seems as though D'Indy had
within himself, together with his essential fineness, a vast

fund of hate and prejudice which insists on manifest-
ing itself, and gets persistently between him and the
object of his thought. He has seen fit to mingle theology
liberally with musical theory. His "Cours de Composition" commences with a demonstration of the reality not
of the major triad, but of the Christian trinity. The
decadence of musical art, he pretends, is due the Protes-
tants and the Jews; for Bach was a Protestant only by
chance, he insists, and Beethoven remained all his days
the Catholic he was baptized! Into the origins of the
Gregorian chant, he will not look. During the war, he
yelled with the throng. He wrote a "Sinfonia Brevis de
Bello Gallico" whose themes have a tendency to go lost
after a half dozen feeble measures of life, but which
nevertheless stirs patriotic emotions for *poilus* in the patriotic breasts. He advised America to rid herself the
sooner the better of the baneful influence of German
music and German musicians, which was petty of him
and also comprehensible to us. For he himself remains
deeply indebted to Schumann and to Wagner for many
a hint. And so when we read in his book on Franck the
lines "La Haine et la Doute, ces négations, s'ils ont
parfois détruit des choses utiles, n'ont jamais pu rien
édifier de stable; seuls l'Amour et la Foi ont pu enfanter
et fonder les œuvres immortelles," we read and smile.
For we recognize it for one of those statements which
are unconsciously made by folk more for their own
benefit than for that of others; one of those phrases
which they call into their own ears in the hope that
something which needs to know it will hear.

Fortunately, Vincent d'Indy has not always been deaf
to this cry of his mouth. The moments of wrong-headed-
ness may have come upon him as oftentimes as yellow
thunderstorms come over fields during wet summers.

They have not, however, prevented the blue from shining daylong unflecked. There is a D'Indy other than this bigot. And it is with him we have business; for he has done work that fills us with a sense of profoundest thankfulness for the high breathing-spaces it offers us. This man has made music that pushes back the incrushing world from about us; and, in the space it clears for us, lets some sense of calm and beauty without which we perish rebuild itself within. We are not men when we cannot bring to life something of a spirit reverend and large and dignified as that which breathes high through his art. The best of us is dead when we forget the beauty of quality. He makes dry streams to trickle and flow again. And so, his music carries within itself a preservative which promises to transport it, through years and weathers, in the august company of those things which are useful to the human being that would live.

July, 1920.

The Fate of "Mona"

ONE more time, the gods showed themselves indulgent towards America. Ten thousand dollars bought a work of art. Money brought forth the best music which had been written by an American.

Explain it as we try, the event, to-day, even, still seems miraculous. It is true that Professor Parker had been experimenting for many years with the setting of English verse in songs; and that in "Hora Novissima," he had shown that he could sing with a maleness and richness of color never before brought to music by an American. Nevertheless, "Mona" could not have been foretold from either of these facts. Parker had not been successful in his songs. He had been trivial, and not, as he wished, Old English, in "The Lark Now Leaves His Watery Nest"; banal-effusive in "I Will Come Back"; closeted in "Across the Fields." And the cantata was written in a vein which might easily have refused to permit itself to be conducted to dramatic forms. Besides, prize money has never been good bait. Work which has to await its golden shimmer before it can get started has rarely come from deep. In their soberer moments, the directors of the Metropolitan Opera House must have faced the fact that the sum offered by them for the best opera by an American composer on an English libretto would probably stimulate the Herberts and the DeKovens and perhaps the Converses, but exert no greater lure.

And still, the ten thousand dollars produced a work of art. Money brought forth music. Money brought forth not only the soundest music written by an American up to the time of its appearance, but one of the best modern operas, worthy to march across the sea and take its place by the side of "Pelléas" and "Elektra," "Berenice" and "Ariane et Barbe-Bleu." To be sure, the work thus acquired through the indulgence of the gods is not the perfectly thrilling and loosening piece one might wish to have. That the structure contains unsatisfying elements is not to be denied. The libretto supplied Professor Parker by Brian Hooker, so much admired at the time of the production of the opera, is at best a sort of pseudo-poetry. The kernel of feeling in it is dressed up in the ladies' nightgown of inherited soulfulness; and we have a great many little groping baby hands and perhaps all souls are shadows and a woman might have won. It pretends to thought; to an arraignment of what was then called militant suffragism. But its thought is pseudo, too. To the "masculine protest," which it attempts to excoriate, it opposes a sort of passive male egoism which is just as silly as the female. Gwynn, the hero, is, it seems, the son of the Roman governor of Britain; and, according to Brian Hooker, "what he is" ought to have had some political significance for the rebellious Britons whom Gwynn is seeking to pacify; and turned Mona into a loving wife and her rowdy compatriots into peaceable subjects. However, they find it out too late; and poor Gwynn lies flat; and Mona left alone, sees the mistake into which her insanity led her, and is, very properly, ushered off to death.

The music, too, is not invariably lovely in quality. Parker was an organist; and his affection for the black, vacant, ecclesiastical instrument intruded itself between him and the orchestra. Not a little of his writing has the thick quality of organ phrasing. He was a Puritan

of New England; and the ramparts erected in his blood
reveal themselves from time to time in the slightly
psalmodizing vein which ducks in and out. Particularly
are they forced upon one's attention by the weaknesses
of the lighter portions of the work, in particular the prelude in Act II and the dance and soliloquy of Nial.
Whereas he was able to do the greatest justice to the
graver and more impassioned moments of the drama, the
composer could not quite succeed in limbering himself to
the dance, and to the capricious and fantastic sublunary.
Moreover, unfortunately, he did not have quite enough
of the objectivity of mind he ought to have brought to
his work. It is probable that he was very sick and weary
of the kind of insurgency typified by his heroine; and
ran a little dry when he came to the scenes of frenzy
and of revolt. The music which ends the first and the
second acts is certainly less effective than the music of
Mona's dream, and the love duet, and the music of Act
III. Of course, Parker was a composer and knew how
to use his material; and nearly every one of his principal
themes are finer in their contrapuntal deformations than
in their primary states. Nevertheless; and even though
the thematic material is in itself sufficiently contrasted
and varied; the themes of Mona's protest well opposed
to those of Gwynn's love for her; the music of the swarming Britons well opposed to the heavy regular march
movement given the Roman soldiery; the work suffers
from this unevenness of inspiration.

Both strength and weakness of the score are exhibited
in the prelude to the first act. Here, sheep and goats are
chained together. The poetical introduction in b-major
is succeeded by a theme in G that suggests not a little
"Hymns Ancient and Modern," and Sunday evening

song-services. And yet, subsequent to the broad climax, there comes a passage, metallic, bitter-savored, pentatonic in mode, which is a piece of ripest inspiration. It is music entirely Parker's own, and of a newness and a largeness that command instant attention. Passages of this quality are what gives the score its weight. To-day, one's admiration for the little opera is greater even than it was at the time of the production, in 1912. Time has worn away none of the high nobility of "Mona." The score has borne well acquaintance and study. Parker indeed wrote a number of pages whose colors cannot run. The love scene with its glamorously straying voices and pearly pianissimos; the strong mournful prelude to Act III, the orchestral outcry that follows upon the murder of Gwynn, with the bitter brasses cutting sheer across the orchestral line, stand untroubled.

And what Parker gave, has a coloration entirely individual. The orchestra, with its reinforced brass and pair of tubas, has a fine ruggedness of sound. There was a strain, something like D'Indy's, in Parker, mixed in with something softer and more Gaelic; and when it did register itself unimpaired, this strain produced a quality of music which in its fine asceticism, its spare passion and ruddy tang, stands quite apart. Above all, Parker's is a *drama per musica*. Not only are action and music married in his score; but word and music as well. Mona's narrative in Act I seems to us one of the most successful marriages between word and music in the story of music among the Anglo-Saxon peoples. Throughout, Parker worked always to bring out the values of the text, to achieve a musical declamation, a recitative style true to the genius of English speech, orchestrating lightly the accompaniment to the declamation in order

not to submerge the voices. What he achieved constitutes, with all its faults, a sort of red letter in the history of Anglo-American musical art.

When the directors of the Metropolitan offered the
prize which drew forth this fine work, they promised the
prizeman performance. Early in the spring of 1912,
therefore, "Mona" was mounted. The season died a few
weeks after; and "Mona" was permitted to lapse from
the repertory. It had not even then been given a proper
chance. Alfred Hertz conducted, it is true. But the
principal rôles were assigned to some of the American-
born members of the troupe. And these helped bury the
work by their incomprehension. The best of the singing-
actors was Albert Reiss, who showed some feeling for the
part of Nial. The scenery was as silly and useless as
the scenery of the Metropolitan inevitably is.

You will say: the unrecognized masterpiece. But
"Mona" was not unrecognized. They knew what they
had, Messrs. Guilio Gatti-Casazza and Paul Cravath.
Did they not place upon record their satisfaction at having acquired the work for their house? And they were
not alone in their satisfaction. Every one felt the
gravity, the virility and the severity in the music, felt it
through the mediocre presentation. Every one seemed
to know that Horatio Parker was something which had
not before happened in American life; and that "Mona"
was a work which might be shown Europe with legitimate pride. The composer had been an eminence in
inner musical circles even before Oxford created him
Doctor; his opera made him a personage before a greater
public.

And still, recognized although it was, Parker's opera
has met a fate not really different from that which meets
works unrecognized of the world. No opportunity was

given it to establish itself. It was not carried over by
the Metropolitan even one season. No attempt was
made to find for it interpreters better than those who
sang it at the première. Not a soul among the directors
exerted himself for it. To-day, Horatio Parker is dead;
and the Metropolitan shows it entertains no feeling of
responsibility toward his work. It called his opera into
existence. But it plays Jean-Jacques with its offspring.
It never occurs to Gatti-Casazza to show a new generation of music-people what America has produced; to
mount the work from time to time as European opera
houses mount the unpopular classics, and let the public
taste correct itself. The critics who found "Mona" wonderful seem to have forgotten entirely their moment of
faith and enthusiasm. Yale University, for which he
spent himself, has done nothing to revise his masterpiece. Not a one protests, and calls the opera back onto
the boards. It might never have been written.

If you will listen, you will hear a great many voices
protesting their desire for the appearance of an American
music. Every one is eager to see a harvest of flowers
spring from our bare soil. Over the country the summons goes, and composers are entreated and harangued
and beseeched that they give us a native musical expression. There are prizes for musical compositions as there
are prizes for paintings and poems, novels and biographies. There are academies, too, wherein people can
get instruction in the art of composition, just as there
are academies where they can learn to draw and paint
and sculpt. There are orchestras, too, endowed to play
American works, just as there are, too, museums built
to house canvases and sculptures. Money has been
poured out; orations delivered; summons given; a youth
entreated to send up artists for the common weal. But

do not let yourself be deceived. Do not take seriously the voices shouting for an art. Nothing is meant by the words. No one really wants it except a few people, and they have nothing at all to do with academies and prizes, orchestras and museums. It is not the verbal declaration that proves that art is wanted.

What alone proves the want is the evidence that there exists a sense of responsibility to the artist; a love for good work which answers the love which brings good work into the world, and makes the community fosterfather to the product, and renders it faithful to the worker in his lifetime and after his death. And the American possessed of a sense of responsibility to the artist is still far. The American possessed of a sense of responsibility to the American is still far. And the two are identical.

August, 1920.

The Concert Hall

I

A MUSTY discolored presence inhabits the American concert hall. It swags from the ceiling like a rain-heavy cloud; clings to walls, to balconies, to carpets; rolls underneath the stalls; and pervades the house with enervating melancholy. Year upon year it persists, too heavy to be lifted, too torpid to be expelled. The hubbub of the season makes not a dent in it. Trumpetings of ruddy brass, roaring of horns, chants of joy, little birds flying out of singing mouths, world-devastating lamentations, conductors waving their arms and pianists smiting the "great black piano *appassionato*"; all the apparent fire, movement, ecstasy of the business leaves it established more massively than ever. It is there before the lights are switched on for the reception of the audience. When the playing ceases and the people file homeward and the electric current is withdrawn, it remains strong, undefeated, peacefully munching its cud like a cattle. Even the hermetic closure of the concert hall during warm weather months does not seem to diminish it. You would think it would perish there of inanition, in the close hot darkness, like a sickness in an isolation ward. But when in the cool fall the doors stand wide again, the first of those who enter the place discover it present denser, mustier, heavier established than before, clinging to walls, to balconies, and upholstery as though there had been no summer; and ready as ever

to demoralize with its infinitely sluggish circulation all
who venture near its dwelling.

The concert room in America is the classic wasting-
place of energies. It is a spot where the river of life
is arrested by means of the misuse of the living substance enclosed in musical literature. American society
cannot make proper use of music. Music is like love:
an expression of the state in which we surrender ourselves
in thanks completely to something higher and purer than
anything we have hitherto known. The past, the future,
they are both present. All materials, trees, waters, skies,
are present; enclosed by the moment as by an integu-
ment. The pains suffered, the pangs to come, death
and separation, they are all become good under its sovereign alchemy. There is no war; there is no division;
because there is only the beating of the universal
pulse, the single movement of all things reaching up
into heaven. And America dare not let feelings such
as these be; not even for an instant; not even away in
some corner. Its material machinery is banked against
them; fortified as against the enemy. For what expresses
itself through music, expresses itself, in the field of material activity, through the search for quality. Under
pressure from it, the labor bestowed on things comes to
exist for its own sake absolutely, too. The chair being
turned, the house built, the piece of cloth woven, they
are twisted and moulded that they vibrate sympathetically
with some feeling about the universe, some joy, some
song, some wonder. The world goes half lost so that a
piece of stone, a piece of wood, bring some fulfillment to
the breast, and a world be gained. But woe to the
American who pursues a dream of quality among commercial products, and loves his tools and the stuffs they
bear upon! Let him leap off Brooklyn Bridge and have

it over with, immediately! The competitive system will not have him. Production is made with an eye to quantity, not quality. One must have the most money, the greatest number of Ford cars, the biggest factory. There is no demand for fine things. And let him but listen for an hour to the promptings of his breast, and the sheriff's people will come.

The American has found himself burdened with intensities which he dare not loose, and which nevertheless, crowd upon him incessantly. In every bosom, even the American's, the passions spring incessantly to life, and clamor without intermission for release. They threaten business, for they hate the nickled routine. They hate the mechanization, the repetition, to which they have been subjected by an uncreative society. They wish to be free to re-invent. They wish to try themselves out ever anew and escape the formula. So they clog the wheels, loosen the bolts, threaten the well-being of the machine in numberless ways. Something, therefore, has to be done to dissipate them. In somnambulistic pursuit of a method the American has stumbled upon music, and found a dump. Like all strong stuff, music is capable of becoming a principle of evil as well as of good. In "them that love God" it sends the river of life flashing; calls once more the passions to their high duty; fills again with nostalgia for the heavenly May. But it can be made to lead the stream into a bayou, too, and let it lose direction there. Performed superficially, without great feeling; performed without understanding of the impulse which sent it into the world; without reverence for the men whose central being manifested itself in it, and gave the world a ladder, it wastes the ardours. Under such conditions, it leads the ardours forth in an amount so small that they can do no work; and still sufficiently great that, because of the excursion, their edge goes dull and no serious purpose can empower itself of them. It toys with them; flatters them; prettifies them; and castrates them. No experience ever comes. No intensity great enough to open the self, and penetrate it with another life and cleanse it , comes. No great self-obliterative moment. No touching of the new. Life never arrives at a birth. Feeling merely lingers on the surfaces; paws over old experiences; moves in a circle; brings in nothing fresh; returns upon itself. Music becomes a selfish indulgence.

So, inside the American concert hall there has come to inhabit, sum of the good life wasted there, the dun lugubrious presence. Innumerable holocausts have made it fat. The passions of a thousand composers, misused, averted, undelivered, have gone to feed the swagging torpid cloud. The emanation of a million hard, unclosed natures, afeared of passionate expression, has swollen it. Men have come in the evening to live furtively what their world does not permit them to live out cleanly, and then gone again submissive to society. Women have crowded, afternoon upon afternoon; purchased a little solace, and then drawn their skirts free of the bastard emotion and gone again into bondage and emptiness. For years, now, by day and night, day after day, week in week out, long trainloads of damned passions have been drawing up in the place, and increasing the enormous mass with their contents. With every season, the deposits become larger. Chicago in a year hears not as many freights clatter over her rails as draw up every winter month before the musical dump. And music plays the waster. One thinks of Tolstoy and "What is Art?" An entire industry with money and backers and agents and workmen

has been built up: all this effort resulting in a manner of
mediocre offspring, technically satisfactory enough, but
undistinguished and colorless. One concert depresses
more than another. You go for months without hearing
a fine performance; a piece nobly done. The season
not more than once or twice surmounts the higher organ-
grind. The musicians are doing the audience's secret
will. Energy stored in treasuries of money is strewn
forth, a sacrifice before the mammon. Thousands of
musicians are shunted to and fro, and lay the breath of
their lungs, the strength of their biceps, the cunning of
their fingers on the pile. In New York City, five or six
concerts take place every day; fiddling, singing, tickling
the ivories, playing the band. On Sundays there are
more, generally; an opera concert or two. Boston, Philadelphia, Chicago, San Francisco get nearly as much.
Smaller cities have their share. And in summer, there
are festivals with Rubenstein concertos, stadium concerts,
Chatauquas, summer-courses, six-week conservatories:
unceasing, meaningless flow.

Everything which takes part in musical life seems to
be converted to its proper uses by the dead presence,
and made into a portion of itself. The concert hall is
not unlike one of those valleys which, so we are told, are
filled with gas so poisonous that animal life cannot
maintain itself in range of them, and birds flying high
above fall smitten to earth. The method by which the
happy valley in the city deals death may be different from
that practiced by its mountainly compeers, and far less
melodramatic. The results to animal life, nevertheless,
are no less fatal. Those who breathe habitually into their
lungs the dull gray atmosphere which inhabits there do
not fall rigid. Apparently, they walk much as they used.

Their comings and goings become more numerous, commonly. Out of the guest-conductor, there grows the permanent leader. Out of the stray virtuoso with a shadowy continental reputation, there grows the regular visitor of three annual appearances in Carnegie and three in Æolian Hall and a fame in every mouth. But it is apparently only that the comers remain unaltered. A change has indeed been worked in them. They have their hair; and yet, one could swear that they had been under the ice in the pond all winter, and had come up hairless as the corpses of drowned people do. There is a limb inside that trouser-leg before you, you know; and yet, what is on the platform looks as wavy and as flaccid as a trouser-leg touching the floor of the closet in which it has been hung. The vibrant inner life brought from Europe has been drawn like pith out of the victim. Another has been put in its place. Conductors who arrived from the other shore and played like lions, gradually turn to mud; sell themselves and permit the rich women to dictate their programs to them. Out of this fine talent here, there has become a vulgar charlatan who will do anything for effect, anything "to make a hit," and perform "Les Preludes" because the noise brings down the insensitive house. Pianists begin to play half-heartedly, to substitute pyrotechnics for music, to cultivate little tricks which obtain with the public. Violinists who arrived and proudly played the Beethoven concerto with the Boston Symphony begin making programs upon which the tawdriest, most mawkish numbers figure prominently. Even into the playing of those who struggle against the atmosphere and try not to give in, there creeps a flatness, and slackness. The starch, the quality, the fineness of spirit, has gone out of them. The American concert-hall has gone in.

II

America is the ruin of most of the musicians who venture into her; but America alone is not to blame for the havoc. The musicians themselves are almost as greatly responsible for it. They do not have to be victims. In their art, they possess the flower *Moly*. The shallowness of audiences need not hold them back. With the position of the bow on the strings, the finger-tips on the keyboard, the surfaces can be quitted, and the clouds of the self-obliterative state receive them quite. Beethoven and Mozart can make them to synchronize with the universal rhythm, and breathe the deepest breaths. It need not matter to them whether the audience smites them for their passion with freezing cold, and punishes them with neglect for refusing to transform themselves into amusement mechanisms. They have a better place to go than it can find them. They do not need the approbation. And one does not have always to perform. One can teach, too.

But musicians do not avail themselves of the power in their hands. There is a traitor within the walls of most of them; and it is this traitor that makes it possible for the concert-hall to incorporate them. The impulse, communicated by the people who fill the house, to pervert the uses of art by taming it, is answered from within the persons on the platform by something scarcely less powerful. The musician, too, has a sort of unwillingness to permit himself to be lost in something greater than he. He is the dullest of artists. He is the most incurably, pettily, personal.

The most personal of artists! Reverberations of hellish laughter play about as the phrase comes forth! With what right, they chatter, can one sort of artist be

called more personal than another, when it has been the
melancholy lesson of experience that all sorts are the
most personal? Your great disappointment in the artist,
has it flowed from any fact other than that these men,
seemingly specially occupied with beauty, almost generally prove themselves hatefully small in human intercourse? You had wished to rank them, as they ranked
themselves, in the company of those who give; but acquaintance has shown them among the maddest of those
who want to get for their little personal selves, and desire
to make of their persons centers of things and objects of
the world. You had expected to find men, and you had
found creatures with the façades of men, insisting on
being the woman and the child, too.

The painters, for example. Lawsy, into what a wilderness of precious egos does one not penetrate when one
goes amongst them! The screens may remain up a
while, from fifteen minutes to three months, and paint
a pastoral landscape. Invariably, they fall. And then,
behold! You are come into the dread presence of a
mighty It; one among many mighty Its; absolute, un-
questionable, alone as an idol in a desert of sand. "La
peinture, c'est Moi!" Doubt it, and you have committed
the sin *lèse-majesté*. For the painter lends out his eyes
only so long as glory accrues to him personally. We are
far away from the romantic image of the paint-man:
great brute painting out of the passion of his heart.
Try but to see another man's work by these eyes and
they will be snatched back without ceremony. The impulse to give has never really managed to assert itself.
Diogenes had more chance of discovering an honest man
among his neighbors, than we of finding in all New York
a painter who has great good to say of one of his young
and living brothers. They set you spinning with their

talk. This one "has no color"; this one "no completed form"; this one is "not modern."

The republic of art may fall: the painters cannot unite in battling for an idea. The moment demands coöperation; the painters continue to cut their throats one the other. The prestige of the Academy is gone. The prestige of the dealers is going. The painter is left face to face with the public; and the public is waiting for assurance that the painter is interested in something greater than himself; that an idea and a passion is behind the experiments, and forcing itself out through the color-sense. And the painters continue trying to get something for each of themselves alone. What a sort of life! to be able to hear the inner voice, and then intrigue against every one else who has the power to hear it; to know in oneself the struggle for faith and then behave towards one's co-workers as the public never behaves; to feel beauty and then play society-lady, art-gallery, museum politics! No, it is not the public alone that betrays art. The painters are the money-lenders in the Temple. Small wonder that Leo Stein has evolved a theory that the artist to-day is a nonentity because men with minds do not become artists; that in the Renaissance men with minds became artists only because the tools of science were evolved insufficiently to give them opportunity of satisfying themselves; and that, were they to be born again to-day, the Massaccios and Leonardos and Michael Angelos would have turned immediately to physics and medicine and engineering!

Like the majority of painters, the majority of writers are sick with the personal disease. The precious self has to intrude everywhere into the foreground. Everything is taken personally, blame and praise alike. Of course, only the more insensitive go about blurting forth that

they are the equals of Dostoievsky and Whitman, Nietzsche, and Wagner. Nevertheless, the excessive self-
feeling outwits many a wakeful censor, and manages to
befog with its poison the literary land. You have to do
no more than breathe a breath or two of it into your
lungs, and your best powers leave you. Song goes out
of you. Sense of others goes out of you. Sense of
everything but your own figure goes out of you. There
is nothing left but a sick need of being seen, of being
published, of being praised, of being discussed, of coming into notice in some fashion.

One of the methods of expression commonly taken by
this excessive preoccupation with self is that which gives
itself out as critical utterance. Criticism, as it is practiced by most poets and novelists, is a sort of indirect
self-exhibition. There are some poets and novelists, to
be sure, who do essay the art of giving thanks in a spirit
of impersonality. They remain rare exceptions. Most
of those who attempt it are led unconsciously by their
self-feeling: by a wounded vanity clamoring for revenge,
or by a gratified vanity wishing further to gratify itself
by elevating to public estimation those who flatter it.
The critical goodwill of very few authors is not to be
purchased by flattery; the faculty of judgment not to be
blinded by criticism of their work which happens to
oppose their wishes. If the romancer Arthur declares to
you that the excellent novel of Benjamin is utterly wanting in form, you may be fairly certain that at some time
Christopher came to Arthur and informed him that Benjamin did not consider Arthur's latest novel a perfect
fiction. If the poet Donald calls Egbert's new volume
of charming verse the greatest poetry written by an
American since Whitman's day, you may rest pretty sure

that Ferdinand has told Donald that Egbert considers him, Don, a bigger man than Swinburne.

You, too, can get yourself "hailed," if you but know how to go about the matter. Do you wish to hear yourself called a great critic? I am assuming, of course, that you have done some critical work, and have gotten a little reputation; for if you have no reputation, you cannot get yourself hailed as a great critic. You will be merely a lovely spirit, a man of promise, or an intellectual. But, if you have indeed gotten yourself a hearing, and are therefore a power, and useful, you can get yourself called perhaps the greatest living critic. This is what you must do, to bring the high thing to pass. You must select the name of one of a dozen serious novelists now living in New York City. You must write an article in some prominent literary paper terming the owner of the name the greatest living novelist, the peer of Balzac, Dostoievsky, and Flaubert. That is all. And, sooner or later, and probably very soon, there will appear an article over the signature of your novelist, declaring you the equal in sagacity of Ste. Beuve, Taine, and the other critical giants.

Or, if you are a novelist, and are just publishing a piece of fiction, you can get yourself heavily underwritten. You do not have to appear in print with an article to secure the boost. You have merely to write a letter to one of the aforesaid twelve, calling him one of our great men, referring to his last book as the American "Madame Bovary"; belittling his most successful rival, and condemning his unconverted critic. That is all. And, when your novel appears, it will be "hailed." It will not be called a great novel, it is true. You must resign yourself to that.

He bears no brother near him on the throne,
Who would be saviour of mankind alone.

But it will be referred to as Great Comedy, and better
than everything written by Henry James and William
Dean Howells taken together. Or, should you and your
great novelist happen both to be Jews, it will be termed
a rebirth of the Jewish soul.

III

Nevertheless, the musician is the dullest of the artists,
the actor alone excepted. By his side, painter and poet
seem men of mind. The musician, the performing musician in America, comes very near being a nonentity
among modern men. To be sure, he is the most
pleasant of companions; a nice fellow; an excellent
raconteur; and familiar with amusing anecdotes of
Bülow and de Pachmann. But it is rarely that he becomes a developed human being; a person with an aggressive attitude toward his environment; with an inner
compulsion stronger than the outward bonds. The
manner in which he works in itself tends to keep the
musician stupid. For it tends to keep him personal.
The end-product of the writer and of the painter is distinct from their persons. The book or the canvas stands
by itself. The creator can step away from it. He may
not always dissociate himself from the thing he has
done. Most often, we find him treating the object as
part of his own system, and accepting criticism as a personal affront. Nevertheless, the fact that while he is
doing his work the world is not present to remind him
that he is a person; the fact that he can inhabit for
long whiles spiritual regions where he as an individual

has no reality; the fact that he is not generally present while his work is being received, ties him a little less closely to his person, and makes it possible for him to leave it in experience. He escapes the deadly round of other men's footsteps.

But the musician cannot as easily separate himself from his product. The work lives and dies through his body. It has no clearly distinct life of its own. During instants, while he is playing, the musician may escape. But the audience is there to call him back to himself. He is before them, a person; and they throw directly at his person their coldness and their applause. It is him they smite or thank when they smite and thank his work.

Hence, the musician approaches the concert hall half concurring in the fate that is to overtake him there. Unable readily to dissociate himself from the thing he is doing, he is already prepared for the assumption of a passive attitude toward his environment, and the expenditure of his vitality in the beaten round. To drag one's little self behind one is to remain in the sphere of what has already been done. Life is only in the sphere in which one cannot enter, a single separate person. And, on the doorsill, the musician meets, symbol of the American concert hall, the patroness. You remember the Symposium, do you not, and its account of the fate of Orpheus? "Now Orpheus, the son of Œagrus, the gods sent back from Hades with his object unaccomplished, by showing him the phantom merely of his wife, for whom he went, and not restoring her real self; because he appeared to act the coward, as being a harper, and not daring, like Alcestis, to die for love, but continuing to go alive to Hades. Hence, on this very account, did the gods impose on him a punishment, and caused his death to take place at the hands of women." With the descendants of Orpheus it goes much as it did with their ancestor. The circle is complete long before they face the audience. The presence of the woman at the door of the concert room seals their fate. For it brings with it the havoc of confused living. It is the expression not of a friendliness, but of a fear of the artist. Were American civilization able to enter the state of which music is the portal, it would send to meet the musician the patron, the creature united and single toward life, and capable of carrying music forward on the crest of a single and intense desire. Being unable to do so, it sends him the patroness, embodiment of its bifurcated and divided interest. It sends him the partner of the business man; dissatisfied with the business man because he is merely the business man, but incapable, because she is his partner and has borne him children and is held to him by the secret American fear of the completely developed human being, of concentrating a complete interest in anything or any one. She is looking for the artist, the patroness; but hiding from him, too. Unable to lose herself in anything, her interest in him remains personal; sometimes an innocent interest, sometimes not quite so innocent a one; but at all times a limited affair. That is what Leo Blech wished to signal when he said, "In Europe, when a musician and a lady have a love-affair, she gets a baby; in America, when a musician and a lady have a love affair, he gets an orchestra." About the musician, the patroness spreads the unhealthy atmosphere of a superficial and selfish interest. In him she unwittingly encourages half-power. She does not live for his art. The apples fall into the hands of those who know how to place themselves to advantage underneath the apple tree. And so, it is the artist of personal charm and social manner, the man who wears a frock coat perfect of line and tinkles brilliantly over the tea cups, who benefits chiefly by the regiment of women in the concert hall. The concert hall has little effort to make when finally the musician appears inside it. He comes trussed and seasoned for the gray death.

IV

The medium which ought to be pouring out one of the great countercurrents to the American anarchy has itself been captured by that anarchy, and made its confederate. Many times, one would, if one could, close the concert hall entirely and banish the musician crowned with roses beyond the frontiers of the republic, so much have he and his art helped to rivet upon us our bad old system. And, unfortunately, they are like to continue doing so, with ever increasing effectiveness. The great traditions of the art have been let dwindle. There are no more lions in the forest. The public has been permitted to become more used to the sluggish circulation of the concerts; and the more concerts, the more sluggish the circulation.

A human being living through music might break the circle, and dominate from the concert hall the machine just as the machine from its place has dominated music-making. There was scarce any point of congress more noxious to life than the opera-house before Wagner entered it and made a temple of the house of show, and, there, awoke a nation to its proper life. It was life to him that the opera should become a point of light, and death that it should remain a means for the self-exhibition of virtuosi; and a musician for whom the health of the concert hall in America were a matter of

life and death might succeed in making it glad with
rarest air. Of course, it is a foolhardy act, this summons to a Richard Wagner of the concert room. We
know that "times have called for their great men, and
they have not come." We know that he will not come
for the asking. Nevertheless, it is always for the man
we wait; the man outside ourselves, inside ourselves; the
man from among the unborn, from among the living. If
it is true that "nature forms creatures only; it is with art
that man begins," it is equally true that it is only with
the human being that art begins its course. And, so,
we wait.

V

Meanwhile, as we watch, this fact is certain: you do
not have to travel to feel America. You do not have to
see Pittsburg, Chicago, and the Grand Canyon to know
the state of life in her. You have to go no further than
round the corner, to the institution called the concert
hall, to have it clear as in a retort before you. America
is here and now. The colors come and go. Sudden
shoots of fire light up the dark. A talent, a sincerity,
a passion comes. Life comes in Beethoven and Bach
and Mozart; life comes in the energies of thousands of
men. The stuffy visages remain. Nowhere can you see
more exquisitely, more poignantly the show upon which
we are all fixed, the beating of the bright bird spirit in
the hands of the immovable mass called American civilization.

Here bring your dreams. Here come, when some
event has made you sing that a new life is in America;
when some comer has brought again belief that man can
change; and fineness be loved; and beauty come up

from poor soil. In this place expose the infant hope. He will probably die. The risk is great. The people are like intractable beasts. But the risk is worth your taking. For, if your dream should persist when the two hours are over, you will have utmost corroboration. You will know that it is no fantasy, but real as the rock. For you will know that you have put it to the severest test to which it could have been exposed; and that it has survived the ordeal by concert.

September, 1920—December, 1921.

The Bloch Viola Suite

An orchestra is lovely to behold as it sits tuning up for an afternoon concert. Whilst the running sea of frustrate lyricism, languid scales and flute quavers and ariosos on the clarinets, rises from off the platform, the hemicycle of musicians itself is a massive harmony. In the soft flushing tone of the enormous chandeliers, the men and their fiddles and reeds form subtle chords of black, of tawny gorgeous golden brown, and flashing nickle and brass. The delicate curves of 'cellos and harps and double basses play against the human shapes. The pungent tones of waxed and seasoned wood, the silver of woodwind keys, the glitter of coiled brasses, oppose the array of broadcloth. Viewed from the balconies, the company of men and tubes and trumps deployed upon the grades of the stage looks a grave magnificent machine, a Velasquez king hung with chains of precious metals over his somber stately dress. Evenings, the harmony is lost. The papery white of the boiled shirts and shirt-fronts lets flatness in. The juxtaposition of 'cello-waists and silver-fretted reeds to noblest black is enfeebled. Only in the afternoon, for a few minutes while seats slam and programs rattle and voices rise, does modern life out of ordinary stuffs compose itself in rich spaces upon the concert stage, and give the dark and shining organism spread thereupon the dignity of an overlord prepared for the reception of an embassy of state, or of a vested priest treading calmly to the altar.

It never remains the pattern it was, once the perform-

ance proper is under way. Usually, it loses utterly its
dignity and splendor: becomes broken into trivial and
grotesque fragments. One becomes aware of the waving arms of the manniken on the podium; aware of the
color of his hair. One sees portly gentlemen who look
like Tchaikowsky and Rimsky sawing furiously across
the strings of their double basses. One sees the extended
leg of the concertmaster as he dandles the little violin
solo on his brown boxlet. Three chesty Teutons elevate
their trombones simultaneously before their faces and
blare the auditorium full of something which really need
not be so explicitly stated. The flutist was probably the
model for the fifer in "The Spirit of Seventy-Six." The
timpanist is busily concocting his little broths in the
cauldrons up in the corner.

But, occasionally the decomposition of the picture does
not take place. Twice or three times at least every
season, the gravely beautiful pattern remains visible to
the eye; grows rather than loses through what is in process
of motion. Then, the side of a viol, the bell of a horn,
play magically into one's consciousness as the field of
stars by the foliage masses of nighttime tress, the rose
light on clouds above bright January snow, play into
moments of profound experience gained beneath them;
and like these radiant visions intensify the ecstasy. The
scene down under the shaded lamps has become wonder-
fully unfolded and transformed. The world is dynami-
cally present upon these boards. The design of blacks
and golden lights is merely a veil, behind which the stream
of modern life where it is most dense and bitter and common flows noiselessly, like a moving picture. It is as
though tunnels have been thrown open through the walls
painted to counterfeit old Gobelins; and across the dim
hall there had been carried on an invisible viaduct, the

trucks and packed sidewalks and sheer stonework of lower Broadway. And the matter actually on the stage has become transmuted strangely into sensitive plasm, a nucleus of throbbing cells and veins with quivering tentacles outspread: very part of the essential substance of all the moving things in the boundless spaces beyond the hollow lighted cube.

A mystical unfolding of the sort took place upon the platform of Carnegie Hall the afternoon Bodansky and Bailly and the National Symphony performed Ernest Bloch's suite for viola. They happen always when performances are a deed of life. And, that afternoon, what went on down upon the stage was not a separate thing, "music." It was something of a piece with what one had lived outside of the hall in a thousand important and unimportant moments. It was like what one felt whenever the thick warm rags over the eyes were cut by experience, and one saw what things were and how they proceeded. And yet, the suite is not the rude, powerful, vehement Bloch. Those who know the barbaric genius of the Genevan only through the "Psalms" and "Schelomo," will find the suite the release of a smaller, less blood-hot and grandiose emotional sum. The work is more objective than any composed by him. One feels him well above the music, controlling it with impersonal hand; but the forms are not as large as those of the string-quartet and the 'cello rhapsody. The four movements, solid and well-wrought though they are, are relatively small in scale.

Still, the suite is one of the most masterfully achieved of Bloch's works. And it marks the commencement of a new maturer period in his life. The quality of this music is that of the earlier pieces. It has the vitality and sincerity of Bloch. It has the harshness and directness, the warm penetrating melancholy, the deep dark oriental sensuousness, of his characteristic idiom. The melodic line is bitter-sweet; the rhythms lift their heavy limbs in frenetic dance; the piled-up fourths pierce the ear with their cruel brilliance. The texture and timbre of the sounds are eastern; eastern not with the sugary orientalism of Rimsky and his fellowship, but with a pungence, a wildness, a subtlety which evokes the desert and the tropical swamp, the lushness and terribleness of the forests of the night, the spice and heat of the straits. The white-robed prophet and the hairy ape both speak.

And the work is more complex and developed a conception than any of Bloch's earlier compositions, the quartet not excepted. A grimacing irony and a light irresponsible gayety hitherto absent from his moods manifest themselves for the first time in the suite; the four movements, homogeneous although they are, show four distinct faces. The first, after the introductory page, with its corkscrew shrilling of fifes, its grave bitter brooding of the solo instrument, its many lamentful tones of blindly groping, bleeding life, is a sort of *gigue triste*. Something dances in relentless activity; something at once an insect swarm in May, and a tribe of little brown men at a phallic feast, and steel bobbins and shuttles. The second movement, the *allegro ironico,* is a variation on the well-known theme "Je m'en fous." An ape-like mockery whinnies through it. Cocoanuts are shied at all the four corners of the world. Some of them display a mysterious tendency to fall near the spot where the apess sits weeping over the children. An acrid trio divides the two sections of the scherzo proper, and concludes the movement. The third is briefer even than the second. It is a *lied;* perhaps the simplest page which Bloch has written. Dark passion throbs on Moussorgsky-like chords of the harp. A nightingale-like cry of the English horn prepares the return of the proud, luxuriant theme; the sensuous hymn dies away again. And the movement which follows on this slow, lovely page springs out like a force released. The fourth movement of the suite is the expression of one of those moods of rapturous gayety, one of those visions of "le pays du soleil" which has been given to agonizing composers before Bloch, to Handel and to Beethoven; and which appear to result not so much from any wending of life itself, as from the victory of their strong minds over their personal griefs. The music of this *allegro giocoso* patters with reckless feet. There are two climaxes. And after the latter, the introductory soliloquy of the solo instrument returns; this time, in clarified and transfigured aspect. In these released and divinely yearnful tones, the savorsome little work concludes.

And the orchestral version appreciated the musical design more than the piano version had done. One already knew, from hearing the latter, how rich the music; the performance by the National Symphony thrust the fact in on one again, and thrust it further. Bloch is determined an orchestral writer; and the pianoforte version of the work, ably as it is executed, adumbrates the colors in place of fully stating them. The orchestral, both swells and subtilizes the ideas; for Bloch instrumentates with the same individuality with which he composes. His style is very rich. Fruits are continually being offered the nostril. And yet, his orchestration is exceedingly sparing and net and pointed. The dynamics of the band, in accordance with the lightness of the musical design, are seldom called into play; the sign *ff* appears only a few times in the score. Nevertheless, the orchestra is felt in its many-mouthed power and variety. Both extremes of coloration are reached. The score brings into play both the shrillness and the somberness of the orchestral sound, and plays them the one against the other. But for all the green flames of flutes traversing the musical texture, the darker colors predominate in the orchestra; perhaps in deference to the timbre of the solo instrument. The difference between the orchestration of Bloch, and that of Debussy, with which it has some affinity, is much the difference between the alto and the soprano voices. There are browns and purples and ancient golds in Bloch's score deeper than those which appear in any of Debussy's. The bass tones of the harp, the nasal baritone of the English horn, the old gold of the solo viola, prevail. Moreover, the use of the instruments of percussion made by Bloch gives his score a sharpness and a briskness quite different from the general character of the tenderer, dreamier Debussy's. The Genevan uses the snare-drum as robustly and as effectively as does Strawinsky. There is a memorable passage in the *allegro ironico* composed of a melancholy recitative of the viola over curious dry taps of the drum. A small wooden box adapted from the jazz bands is employed; in the last movement, in conjunction with the celesta, it cracks over the orchestral mass like a whip.

It was deep into the nutritious bread of reality one bit during the minutes Bailly stood with his viola before the audience, and the brown-golds of the music filtered into the hall. Bloch is one of the few men living in whom the world becomes tone. He is one of the few who hear; who have the art of hearkening to their proper bodies. The most of us, musicians, poets, prosemen, do not know how to hear, how to lean attentively over ourselves. We do not know how to pause suspended and give heed to what the blood murmurs. We are outside, averted, deaf to the fine trickle of song always within the body. We struggle to fit our-

selves into forms bequeathed to us. We persuade ourselves we feel as other men felt, a hundred years ago,
fifty years ago, twenty-five years ago. But Bloch does
that which Bach did, which Wagner did, which Debussy
did, and which every true musician will do. He goes
directly for his substance, his form, to the warm, moist
quick of sensation. He permits himself to be guided not
by what others have felt, or said they have felt, but by
what takes place within his flesh. He is eager only to
hear that murmurous evanescent thing, to seize it in its
immediacy, to fix it in its ineluctable, unfathomable flow,
before it escapes him and us entirely. He hearkens until
his spirit ear becomes sensitive to its wayward flow, till a
continuity, a pattern, commences to define itself in the
chaos. He hears, always in progress in him, the transformation of pain into pleasure, of pleasure into pain; the
unrelenting piling of edifice upon edifice, each superstruc-
ture subsiding immediately to make way for the coming
one; the melting in the solidification, the retreat in the
advance. He hears the pain of the years crystallized into
an incandescent moment of pleasure; he hears the drag of
hours of depression, the movements in him up and down.
He knows what takes place between him and the objects
of New York when he goes out; what the deeds of men
mark in him; what rhythms rise from within to meet the
ugliness, what rhythms come from without and insist
themselves on him and carry him before them. He knows
the state of his life, the submerged, before-dawn light.
And always within him, he is aware of the presence of an
impulse to embrace all things and men, a great will to say
yea. It is perhaps the impulse that realized itself too
romantically, trustingly, in the c-sharp minor symphony,
and which the experience of life, of men, of the world, has

driven in, chained, weighed to earth. But it is alive, and fumbling for egress. It is always there, beneath the bitterness, beneath the melancholy brooding, beneath the pain, beneath the ape-like joy and tenderness, veiled, grand, and sorrowful. And it forces itself upward, lacerated, woeful, half-broken, till at last the doors give, the old prophetic strain stands free and speaks again, stammers with excess, stands silent while the clouds part in the light of dawn.

He is the rare person—the musician who thinks! He is the man who likes to play with tones and who nevertheless is a vivid citizen of the world, liberal in his interests and his knowledge, sufficient to himself, able to wander lonely, indifferent at heart to the fashions of music and to the praise and blame of the public voices. He is the man who expresses courage and honesty in every one of the many forms of a rich existence. No matter what the room of life in which men of the sort of Ernest Bloch find themselves, their manner of conduct remains identical. Hence, when one of such has within him the soaring and the singing of some great feeling about the world and human life; when an adventure, a death, a birth, or, as in the case of the Bloch viola suite, the reading of a book of anthropology sweeps within him the chords of the spirit, he can permit what is actually there to happen as it wants to happen. Fear of strangeness and unusedness does not make him withhold his hand. He dares put it into the warm nest and feels fully of the egg that is there. He dares feel unreservedly, completely, the curve and contour of the growth; to poise the full mass of it in his palm and weigh it with his man.

For this reason, then, a living tapestry was unrolled before our eyes, and a body of men stroking catgut, blowing pipes and winding trumps and horns became a thing of wondrous beauty. The orchestra moving in the intention of a real musician had become a bush aflame; full of the solemn gesture of salutation made by life outside to life within.

November, 1920.

Damrosch Historical Cycle

THE admirers of Mr. Walter Damrosch are used to justi-
fying their regard for him by pointing to his programs.
So finely made are these, they pretend; so original and
catholic, that alone because of them their author ranks
high among conductors. They will have it that entire
fields of music have been opened up for the enjoyment
of the New York public by him. By the general colorful-
ness of his concerts, he has taught the blind to see and
the halt to run. As an educator, they assert, he is great.

As a leader, of course, very few, very few even of his
most fervent admirers, find him satisfactory. The man's
inability to express himself; the absence of rhythm and
coördination and plasticity from the performances which
fill Æolian Hall so many Sunday afternoons with something which resembles nothing quite as much as the Gil-
bertian "bloom on cold gravy," is generally remarked.
Indeed, you will meet with little but sympathy when you
complain of the regularity with which compositions are
muffed and fumbled and still-born at the concerts of the
New York Symphony, and of the absurdly great amount
of the conductor's energy which is turned to self-display.
No one enjoys his little exhibitionistic habits upon the
platform; his majestic and lumbering entrance through
the forest of violins which makes you wonder whether
you have before you Bossuet advancing to pronounce the
funeral oration over Queen Henrietta Maria, and which is
ever so much more impressively managed than the entrance of the first theme of the symphony when it appears;

his trick of facing about during the performance of a work and fixing the audience with his regard—"he is counting the house," the musicians say; his delight in addressing fatuous explanatory remarks to the assemblage. Every one suffers under these attempts of the man to force conscience of his own person on the hearers. But on the score of the program-making, the admirers remain intransigent. Through the freedom and intelligence with which he has made his selections, they maintain, he has made all of us eternally beholden to him.

We need not hesitate an instant over the nice question which immediately proposes itself: the question whether any one who conducts as Mr. Damrosch does, even were he to make programs like an archangel, could succeed actually in developing the taste of his audiences. For the contention of the apologists is falsely based. The programs of the New York Symphony, although livelier far than those of the Philharmonic under the leadership of Mr. Stransky, are neither the handiwork of an archangelic, an angelic, or a very robust human intelligence. They are merely the ordinary concert-programs played by orchestras all over the world, in Paris and Rome and Buenos Ayres; a little more deftly scrambled, and cleverly varied from time to time with novelties. But the novelties introduced are of very unequal value. Many new names and new pieces figure annually at these concerts; but many of the names and compositions have little more than their unfamiliarity to recommend them. The classic repertory is not really catholic and daring. It will be found that Mr. Damrosch remains prudently within the conventional limits, and forays no more often into unknown territory than the average symphony conductor does.

To be assured of it, one need do no more than glance

over the programs of the Historical Cycle given in Carnegie Hall by the New York Symphony during the winter of
1920-1921. The purpose of this cycle, it seems, was to
give the audience a clear sense of the development of the
orchestral language from the time of Rameau to our own.
Now, that the imagination be stimulated and the development dawn upon the audience with edge and freshness, it
is necessary that something more radical, more unconventional than a chronological arrangement of thrice-
familiar compositions, and a grouping of composers in
"national" sets, be devised. The brain-ducts formed by
the constant repetition of certain works have made it difficult for us to hear them. Hearing them grouped in national sets, though it may increase our patriotism by help-
ing persuade us of the divine origin of national boundaries,
does not at all sharpen our ears. For the development of
music has resulted as often from the interaction of
national groups upon each other as from the interaction
of compatriots. National politics do not necessarily make
fellow-musicians. What, then, was required for the making of a Historical Cycle that should be something more
than a fine name given tame matter, was the performance
of the more unfamiliar compositions representative of the
masters; and of the compositions by the great eccentrics,
the men who oftentimes have given a greater impetus to
the development of music than have the more popular
men.

But the concerts of the Damrosch cycle followed in the
ancient ruts. The programs were made up of the old
standard repertory juggled a little. It was the first, the
fifth and the seventh of Beethoven's symphonies which
were played; not the far too rarely presented second and
fourth. There was no Telemann, no Hasse, no Philip
Emanuel Bach. Debussy was represented by the first

two of his Nocturnes—and what conductor does not play the first two Nocturnes, and omit the gorgeous third?—and not by "La Mer" or "Ibéria." Berlioz was represented by "Harold"; Liszt by "Tasso"; Rimsky by two movements of "Scheherazade"; Franck by the "Variations Symphoniques." The errors of complete omission were greater. While Saint-Saëns, Tchaikowsky, Rachmaninoff and D'Indy were included, Chabrier, Bizet, Bruckner, Balakirew, Moussorgsky, Borodin, Dukas, Magnard, Strauss and Bloch were completely snubbed. Haydn was practically neglected in figuring only as composer of the "Clock" symphony. Strawinsky figured merely as composer of the early "Firebird." While Chadwick, Hadley, and Mr. Damrosch himself stood on the American program, Parker and Gilbert were excluded.

It is, therefore, inevitable that we find Mr. Damrosch maker of programs not the great superior to Mr. Damrosch conductor, which his partisans pretend him. In this function, too, we find an inexpressiveness like that which characterizes the other. For in the sphere of program-making, too, the accent seems to have been placed on the personal exhibition; on the looks of the process rather than on the thing being done. And where the accent is so placed, there seems, invariably, to result something which has the nature always more of a simulacrum than of a verity.

November, 1920.

Cyril Scott

SCOTT is a Parnassian when he is most strong. His sonata for piano and his piano concerto are at once opulent and marmoreal. Their beauty is a beauty of pomp and slow proud gesture and orotund period taken musical shape. Fire and sheet-ice combine in them; surface fire of enthusiastic sweep and crashing ecstatic summit and Handelian state overlying the profound personality and chill of the poet turned away from existing fact into regions of grandiose and indifferent and solitary dreaming. They are *Übermenschenmusik,* like some of Szymanowski's and Scriabine's orchestral compositions; arrogant and voluptuous and flauntful; rhythms of runners stepping through the skies far over human heads; visions of the glory of the creative life; visions profoundly uninformed of the depths of the heart and of suffering and brotherliness and man. A marble being made them, too, and what they utter is eloquent of some cold and sumptuous palace of art where rags and sores and muddied feet never penetrate, and the heaped treasures of the world are used to procure in life's despite a perpetual dalliance. They have their kin in the actions and dreams of a generation of gods and impotents: Louis II building Versailles on the Chiemsee and Neuschwanstein in the lonely heart of the mountains; D'Annunzio cradling himself with visions of a Pentelican temple on the shores of Como dedicate everlastingly to his own dramatic art; Stefan George upholding in solemn verse before a yellow curtain a hieratic and glorified image of himself. A trifle belated, these English scores arrive and assume their place by the side of much old-fashioned grandeur.

And they have beauty, even though it is a beauty circumscribed and shut off from the electric reaches of to-day. The stuff of them is rich and good. Generally, the material excites us with its native amplitude and density. Scott is one of the creatures born to musicianship. Many living musicians are more respectable and vital artists than he. Nevertheless, his Sunday-childhood sets him among the rare few. What he has in his fingers cannot be obtained with will. It falls from the gods; and remains in the touch of its host as felicity and glamor and magic. Music comes from this man, wan and languid, it is true, but molten and relaxed in its flow. It is born out of the cool stony beauty of the piano-sound. The ideas are just fallen right, right in the register, right in their harmonic vesture. Song begins tender and magical in him; auditory sensations are caught. Delicate washes of beauty, glintings of rich novel harmonies, brilliant orchestral hues, appear as though shaken out of a sorcerer's bag. Scott's harmonic progressions thrill mid the flamboyant forms; fill with their power and subtlety. He is among the original modern harmonists; sometimes acrid and pricking; oftener, juicy and gorgeous. The color is always rich, whether color of harmony or of instrument. There is a fine cloudy sonority in the middle movement of the concerto, with its noble bell-tones; and the last movement rings bright with the well-disposed sounds of celesta, campanella, harp and piano. At moments, power cries out of these works. Page upon page of the piano sonata, the opening theme, and passage precedent to its return, the staccato triplet passage toward the close of the second movement, proves him capable of not only the dreamful, tender lyrical movements, but of the large aggressive exuberant ones as well. The final fugue is masterly, almost; piles rock on rock in its racing ascent.

Unfortunately, it is a disheveled beauty that comes to us in Scott; in the very best of his compositions. It does not even fill out the sphere to which it is limited. Between the magnificent stuffs there are holes. The satins and velvets and gilding are strewn about disorderly, and do not play properly against each other. Scott's thematic invention is unequal; his critical sense uncertain. The sonata for piano, the very best of his works, shows how weak both are. The themes of the first movement are satisfactory and well contrasted; the heroic first motif plays against the languorous second; grandiloquence and fire against the dreamful and wayward flute. But in the second movement, the composer becomes the mawkish Englishman, pompous and episcopal; and the Englishman never becomes sentimental but he empties the suddy-pail entire, to the last soapy drop. Later, Scott simpers, "vesperal" with MacDowell; and the fugue has to erect its ladder to hardier regions midmost a pool of melted sundaes.

More responsible for the disarray is the absence of the formal sense. Both sonata and concerto are without genuine organization. Clangorous and opulent and sensitive as the music is, crammed with rich lyrical substance, with pearly and opalescent color, it wants base. It has no situation in space; no points of departure and rest and conclusion. It is like an array of large unanchored fragments; pieces and progressions of sound which start out bravely enough, but complete no curve. Little that Scott touches and that quivers a minute in his hand, is maintained. The pulsing lyrical fragments rarely build out, continue and engender each other. The earth, pressed a brief instant, fades. Each fresh idea is always something of a new commencement. The middle movement of the concerto is curiously indeterminate, ends up in air. The finale is somewhat like a railroad train which starts to circle the globe, but being too rigid to conform to the curvature of the earth's surface, quits the ground and loses itself in the chill regions of interstellar space. The concluding measures of the work, the recapitulation of the opening Handelian chords, tastes arbitrary and not satisfying. While the first movement of the sonata hangs together, the second goes quite to pieces. The pages which precede the fugue are both lone wandering and being lost; an impasse of sound; endless repetitions of indeterminate phrases. And, as in the concerto, the rapid, acrid, brilliant finale does not really come to a result. The peroration, noble and exciting as it is, seems, here too, an arbitrarily harnessed coda.

Imagination is wanting Scott; for that reason his very major works retain the general character of brilliant improvisations. His gift has remained an almost purely physical thing. He is the slave, it appears, of his two hands. What they, wandering over the keyboard, find for him, and not what his mind shadows forth, is determinate for his work. He cannot project a rhythm away from himself, outside his body; cannot conceive a work in such a fashion that it has a shape its own, iron and immutable. Form, after all, is the product of the marriage of a rhythm projected by the brain well before the process of incarnation is begun, and of a steady and unflagging improvisation lying in the curve projected by the brain. And Scott, incapable of real imagination, has, it seems, to permit one phrase to suggest another, and to construct his works in fairly haphazard fashion.

And when once a figure manages to establish itself in his work, it has the tendency instead of flowing and generating complementary figures, to become obsessive. The two passacaglias for orchestra seem born of such rigidity. They have the "hammering monotony" of a single figure repeated over and over with exasperating unvariedness. In them, the *basso ostinato* of "The Jungle," effective enough in the piano composition, has a counterpart almost maddeningly regular. The form of the passacaglia, one supposes, demanded something other; demanded a steady variation of theme and deformation of rhythm. Now, Scott has indeed varied the orchestral dress of the tunes, the "Irish Famine Song," and the "Poor Irish Boy," upon which he has based the passacaglias. He has lavished the colors of the grand orchestra upon them, particularly those of the instruments of percussion. The pianoforte is brilliantly introduced in the second. But the monotony persists, despite the steady augmentations of volume which brings both compositions to resonant conclusions.

In the effort to correct this imaginative poverty and invertebracy, Scott has had recourse to mechanical expedients. He has attempted to create a great irregularity of beat in his works; to contrast five fourths with four fourths and seven eighths with five eighths and eleven sixteenths with nine sixteenths, and so forth. But the result, as in all instances of mental protestations against imaginative impotence, is thoroughly unhappy. There is no real justification for the continual changes of time in which Scott indulges. The shifts are not invariably justified by the musical phrases. Often, the irregular bars reveal themselves as perfectly arbitrary; purely wilful extensions of regular ones. Hence they defeat their own purpose. Intended to lift the music out of the rhythmical ruts into which it has the tendency to fall, they create a sort of monotony of their own. For they are not necessary. But, so it seems, Scott harbors a theory to the effect that there is a need for these changes; and, if not necessary, interesting, at the least; and finds a sort of occupation for his unrooted mind by acting upon it. And, as usual, the over-determined act is quite as truly expressive of the inner condition as the one it is calculated to correct. You cannot lie to life.

The composer whom Scott most resembles is Mac-Dowell. His general evasiveness makes the Englishman the successor to the American. Scott is the richer talent. But the evasion of the earth, the retreat from the ruthless line and the naked word is strong in him, too; and his compositions remain with us a modernized version of the sweet, wan, profoundly unsatisfactory little pieces in which MacDowell spoke his native tongue. He too, cannot build. He, too, splendid though his gesture, is one of the somewhat yeared adolescents of music. And with a sigh for the good treasure left lying wingless, we resign ourselves to having another composer who will leave us always unfilled: for the reason that a power of which life has greatest need never came bringing gifts to his sumptuous talent.

December, 1920.

The Strawinsky Concertino

THE audience which heard the Flonzaley Quartet play Strawinsky's Concertino expressed its dislike frankly and flatly. The traditional method of damnation with faintest applause, of exclusion with low quasi-hysterical guffawing, was superseded extensively by some you know un-Anglo-Saxon hissing, which increased in vehemence and drowned quite the laughter when the members of the quartet made faintly as though to recommence the short composition. The clear-eyed, clean-jawed American business man, usually prompt only with his tears, his handclapping, and his flapper-like exclamations of "Oh, isn't that *just* too *lovely,*" forgot his timidity for the nonce, and hissed. His sisters and his cousins and his aunts, ladies blonde, brunette, and grizzled, supported him with an amazing alacrity, and issued in the direction of the platform where stood the embarrassed Flonzaleys some longdrawn, handsomely sustained sibilations. Each row of stalls seated at least one individual who declared roundly to a circle of approbative listeners that "if he ever saw that composition announced on a program again he would stay away," and defied the musicians to do without his two dollars. Indeed, feathers stood dangerously ruffled, every one looked "what the devil does Betti mean, anyway," until the performers began making amends by watering the 1840 rosebuds of the Schumann a-major quartet, and left the audience to dream fondly, eyelids shut, lips parted, on grandmother's bridal veil.

Something had been sharply, savagely relieved in the

concertino. The fiddles had spoken bitterly; futility. They had spoken angrily: boredom; spoken: the joke of it all. The Strawinsky music is a drab, rasping, tired shuffle and breakdown. It is like a locomotive which has fallen off the track, leaving its wheels to revolve in air. Rhythms prolong themselves out of sheer inertia; pound on, wearily. A lyric coda of a few measures, a sort of momentary illumination of a darkened landscape, breaks off into silence just as it begins to establish itself. Petrushka, seedier, older, sullener, is on the boards again, dancing. Before the war his mad energy used to come out of him in forms of beauty. The frenzied desire for release with which he threw himself against the walls of his prison was terrible and wonderful. But now, his energy comes out of him in ugly gestures. He no longer deems it worth his while striving for escape. He is grown vindictive. He dances—because he was born with his mind in his feet; and also, because he is hungry. But he loses interest in his dance long before his feet cease shuffling and beating. He asks himself bitterly, "What's all this for?" while his feet continue for some reason to execute the movements. The machine continues of its proper momentum long after the meaning of its activity has been lost. At the end, Petrushka summons himself to speak. He wants to say something conclusive about life, to seize the spark of emotion which suddenly glints in him. He commences "Oh, Life!—" then stops short. There is so much to be said that it serves no end to speak. There is nothing to be said at all. Finis—the world for him. Finis—perhaps for all men. Finis—of a certainty, a civilization.

The concertino furnishes another example of Strawinsky's happy gift of forgetting the musical past, of finding light, intriguing, incisive musical form, and of revealing life with amazing and disarming simplicity thereby. The brief mordant movement for the four strings comes to us dyed with the acrid hues of the European mess. It is a splinter of mirror in which there is reflected something of the enfeebled state of life in the years which succeeded the armistice. Strawinsky is an artist. He "does not do what others consider beautiful, but what is necessary for his own peace of mind." He has to get things out of himself and away from himself; he has continually to rid his bosom of perilous and intoxicating stuff which threatens to choke it. And what he brings out from within himself has in it in some strange fashion something germane to people, something they are the cleaner and freer for hearing at last. Some of his recently produced music, the childish, humorous "Pribaoutki," the lazy piano-pieces with their satirical echoes of moving-picture symphonies, the naturalistic animal-fable, the tawdry, tender "Histoire du soldat," have no doubt a certain intellectual basis. They constitute a sort of reaction against the music of the decade before the war, and without the war something analogous to them might nevertheless have appeared. Strawinsky is trying to move away from both the jewel quality of the French, and from the pathos and exaltation of his own "Sacre du Printemps." He seems to be following in the footsteps of Moussorgsky in putting down little humorous, naïve, unpretentious things, and setting out in his own way in search of music which shall be vulgar and of the day, of the music-halls, the movies, and their ragtime; ragtime is his "folk song." But there is an element in this music which is not so much part of a reaction from the musical past as it is a reaction from the war and the peace. The sullen and bitter color, the irony, the scurrility, the self-mockery, the expressions of fatigue, and boredom, come out of the agony of disillusionment and impotent resentment brought about not so much by the gigantic wastage of human and material energy, as by the failure of the human spirit, the failure of liberalism to control the machinery of existence. Something like it the Greeks must have heard inside them after their freedom was extinguished by the Macedonians and the Romans. Something like it must have been in the men who went to die in life in the Thebaid during the decay of the antique world. Life is once more seen a thing so mean, so miserable, so silly, that no moment seems any more worthy than any other; and all of no significance whatever. The victories of the Alexanders, the thoughts of the wise men, seem not a whit more worthy of notice than the squealing of the swine in Pyrrho's farmyard. Of no matter the birth of a man; of no matter his death; it would be entirely disproportionate to spend breath in lamenting one's unhappiness. It is, indeed, a sort of modernized pyrrhonism folk feel to-day. One sees it in the posthumous novel of Guillaume Apollinaire, with its mass of trivial and ludicrously unrelated detail. One sees it in the poetry of the dadas, studiedly unselective. It is in the scurrilities of the Group of Six; in the dull grating sarcasm of the Strawinsky concertino.

Certainly, the ugly, infinitely significant music of the concertino is of a piece with the lives of the folk who listened to it that evening in Æolian Hall. The place was more a unit during the performance of the Strawinsky than it has almost ever been, at any other concert. Audience, performers, composition, the tasteless and vulgar decorations of the hall itself, were interwoven, interplaying, doing much the identical thing. A light had suddenly been cast from some secret source, illuminating cruelly matters till then half shadowed. The drabness, the weariness, the joylessness of the music seemed to proceed out of the hundreds packed, as they are packed evening after evening, into the rows of the seats. One perceived the players anew through the music, perceived the want of conviction, the want of enthusiasm, in them. One perceived the audience, starkly, unforgettably. The fatigue, the flaccidity of the American public was underscored. Money one saw; food; complacent coiffures that said "Well, here we are!" But neither youth, nor eagerness, nor joy, nor resiliency, were visible. Wherever in the audience the eye rested, it saw dun, gray, whether it fell on yearless faces or on yeared. People were sitting; everything was sitting. Life was headless, lukewarm, weary from inaction, from inadequate action. One thought perforce of rubber bands from which all elasticity has passed. One saw what America does to young people, to old people. The modern conveniences, dentistry, plumbing, did not awaken respect during those few minutes. Life was what the music was—tired, inane, the weary revolutions of a machine no man can arrest.

And the audience hissed. It did its utmost to punish the musicians who had dared offer them this work. It did its utmost to banish for ever the composition from the concert halls. Not that it had failed to see the implications of the music. On the contrary, it had felt them only too well. And for that reason, it sought to exclude it, to destroy it. The mechanism that makes the American public so hostile to, so neurotically stupid before, the contemporary artistic expressions, was at work in the audience again. The living artist comes to folk with the offer of a contact with the present. He comes to them with the truth of an experience, with the fact of what his life is, of what their own lives are. He comes to tell them what is at work in the world to-day, what the tenure of his own existence is, what is happening or about to happen

to them.   And that is precisely what our musical and
artistic public does not wish to know.   For the persons
who assist at concerts in the United States belong the
most of them to the class of people who assist at entertainments generally in the United States.   And this class
is the class of those who want the world of yesterday to
stand still and not flow away from them, and remain the
world of to-day; not for the reason that the world of
yesterday has given them something of what they want of
life, but for the very reason that it has refused them what
they want of it.   Being unsatisfied, they are full of the
fear of the unknown.   They distrust their powers of cop-
ing with the situations with which life in its evolution is
persistently confronting them.   They think always of the
future.   Nevertheless, something very powerful in them
wants nothing new in the world.   And still, new elements
are perpetually developing in it.   "Normalcy" has not
prevented the ground from shifting beneath the feet of
the million-headed Canute.   They themselves are gradually being ruined by the cumbersomeness of an obsolete
banking system.   The machine is entirely out of their
control.   But, instead of being able to protect themselves
in seeing the state of the world, in viewing themselves as
nakedly as possible and thus preparing themselves for the
encounters, they are in spite of themselves impelled to
play at being ostriches.   They will to abolish things by
keeping them from their consciences.

Hence, the artist who expresses the day is the enemy.
A deep vague resentment goes out against the living new.
Before the war and the peace, the resentment was strong.
The eye and ear were closed when he approached.   The
weakened state of man since the war has doubled its
intensity.   The country is caught in a movement "back to
the sandpile and in with your head."   And since there is

a courtesan in every virtuoso, the performing musicians
will not stand out against it, neither in board meetings nor
on the concert platform.   Mother Goose secures applause,
and therefore, Mother Goose it is that is performed. For,
after all, what is it our audiences demand other than

> Ride a cock horse
> To Banbury Cross

and

> Bye, Baby Bunting
> Daddy's gone a-hunting?

Is it indeed anything other than the repetition of compositions which have been heard so often that no edge
remains to them, no surprises lurk in them, no strangeness
that demands activity of imagination and quickness of
thought? What they demand really is nothing other than
not being forced to have to wonder, to think, to enlarge
their experience, to enter sympathetically into minds not
their own.   Symphonies are repeated with nauseating
regularity, and excite applause infallibly. A sigh of relief
issues from the house as some Fifth Symphony, Beethoven's, Tschaikowsky's, Dvorák's, is attacked.   The
listeners know that they will meet nothing unexpected,
nothing novel, nothing difficult to apprehend, nothing
that will make them stretch their brains. To be sure,
were some one to appear on the platform and recite to
them

> Mary, Mary,
> Quite contrary

or

> Tom, Tom, the piper's son
> Stole a pig and away he run

they would hiss, as they hissed Strawinsky. For the truth
about themselves would be dangerously nigh to dawning
upon them. But, when our "music-lovers" have before
them Stokowski and the Philadelphia Orchestra playing
the musical equivalent for Mother Goose—the moron
music of Dvorák's "New World" Symphony, with its
dulled edges, its ignoble platitudes, its largo that might do
rather nicely at the movies when the old darky dies on the
film, its scherzo with its chorus of wealthy milkmaids—
they sit in bliss, nostrils distended, and rattle applause like
salvos of artillery.

They do not appear to be in the least aware toward
what it is that they are, at the very moment, stretching
out in their throats.

December, 1920.

Three Italian Moderns

OF a sudden, swiftly in the few months of a single season, the Italian symphonists have come upon us. There has been the crash of a breaker-top; and now, everywhere, in every concert hall and under every baton the new works outspread. Casella, Respighi, Sabata, Pizzetti, Pick-Mangiagalli, Malipiero are names which have become perfectly familiar to every one who assists regularly at concerts. Italian music is no longer chiefly old man Verdi and older man Puccini and the anæmic nephew Montemezzi. It is something with an anchorage as distinct and visible among the absoluter forms as in the opera house.

Ripples, it is true, have been outriding the billow that has floundered. For some years now, we have been aware that Italian instrumental music is not merely overtures by Sinigaglia and string-quartets by Tommassini. Not all the newcomers were names, only, to all of the public when finally the tide advanced en masse. There had been a constant seepage of the newer Italian instrumentalists previously into the New York seasons. A tripartite symphonic poem of Zandonai's was given by the New York Orchestra several winters before and revealed the flowers of Strauss abloom on the southerly Alpine slopes. Varèse, in his brief adventure with the New, later National Symphony, attempted to render "Notte di Maggio" by Casella with a lady in a magnificent robe out of Ghirlandajo. Ornstein, in far distant times at Mrs. Reis', played Casella's "Nove Pezzi"; and at one of Casals' too infrequent recitals we were given to hear a sonata for 'cello and piano by the same composer. At the close of the war, there was "Hommage à Marinetti," otherwise known as "Films."

Now, however, the single swallows have become a summer. Due probably as much to the skillfully managed propaganda of one of their compatriots established in American musical life, as to the fact that the number of their compositions available for performance is being increased steadily by their industry, we have had a season given a wellnigh distinguishing color by the attention bestowed on the work of the young Cisalpines by symphonies and chamber-music organizations. "Italia" by Casella, after it had appeared on the programs of practically all the "pop" concerts of the universe, was finally presented to us by the Philadelphia Orchestra. The New York played the suite drawn from his ballet, "Le couvent sur l'eau." Toscanini performed "Le fontane di Roma" by Respighi, and "Juventus" by Sabata. The sonata for violin and piano by Pizzetti was played both by the duet-Blochs and Kathleen Parlow. Of the members of the tribe it is Malipiero who has been the most favored. Three of his pieces were presented. The second set of his "Impressioni dal Vero" were conducted by Bodansky at a concert of the National Symphony. His "Grottesco" for small orchestra was played for the first time in any land by the same leader at a concert of the Friends of Music. The string quartet, "Rispetti e Strombotti," which won the Coolidge Prize last summer, was served up by Letz and his associates. ("Let's alone.") And other works by Malipiero and others of the group are being prepared and held in readiness by other instrumental and vocal organizations.

The new Italians are welcome. They bring much that is brilliant and pricking and amusing. They bring several intriguing profiles; and the promise of many interesting and novel works. At their worst, they bring nothing as stupid as the poor stuff which is regularly and incessantly dished up to us every season. At their best, they bring work daring in conception and well-shaped and sincere. Nevertheless, up to the present, they have brought nothing of primary importance. Their donation falls far below that of the modern Frenchmen in point of originality, power, purity. When Franck and D'Indy, Debussy and Ravel were finally discovered to us and housed among us, there was shown us something more than the fact that men, of a nationality hitherto pretty much unconcerned with the modern instrumental bodies, were at work in the neglected medium. The work was a new-colored substance, a perfectly vital thing wrought by the sweeping movement of power and faith; and revealed, outstretched before us, fragrant tender-hued river-land wherein we might walk.

When first it was bruited about that a new school of instrumentalists was busied in the Italian peninsula, we found ourselves hoping for a recurrence of the miracle performed by those who had imported the French. Perhaps the propagandists for the new music themselves believed they had the stuff wherewith it might be worked. But we were mistaken; and they, too, if they supposed themselves empowered. A new spiritual province is precisely what has not been opened. What has been opened, is a geographical one, merely. The vital sweeping movement, part power and part faith, is wanting Italy. Something new, assuredly, is there. The fine old garlicky brigand Verdi and the perfumed costermonger Puccini no longer transmit the national life entire. The long physical night of the folk is passing. More than all industrial adjustments, more than all mouthings of the imperialists,

the musics of Pizzetti and of Malipiero prove it. The
new instrumental Italians are aristocrats. Whatever their
powers, they are no longer willing to achieve a success on
a low plane. These are not base natures, calculating
syrup for flies, and debauching themselves with raw and
brutal rhetoric. These are men sharing in the best European life, standing on a good intellectual plane, trying to
develop the subtleties of their art and to refine their
thought. They are concerned for their integrity. Though
it costs them their popularity, they will plunge further
into the unknown. Something inside them has rendered
odious to them the practice of their immediate predecessors; and for example and support they find themselves
returning to the noble Italian instrumentalists of the sixteenth and the seventeenth centuries. Not one or two,
but an entire band of composers have set forth to root out
of themselves the meretriciousness which has made the
world for long suspect every Italian musician, even the
most talented, who comes bearing gifts.

But the movement itself is puny, lacking great vitality.
It is, very largely, a reflection; derivative in style. What
brought the new men into life was strong enough to set
them to a new task, but not sufficiently strong to make
them self-determined and productive from their own deep
centers. They are sophisticated; their roots feeble. They
are dependent overmuch on the stimulus of work being
done in other parts of the world. Some one else has always to take the initiative. Then, and then only, can they
act. In their work, racial elements do appear; some consciously, some quite unconsciously employed. But no
bird's nest is fuller of foreign particles than is the music
of the modern Italian school. All sorts of scraps and
atoms of Paris and Muscovy and Vienna are limed together; sometimes cunningly, oftener, crudely. They are

not really worked in, as the ideas and processes of one
man have sometimes been reworked in the edifices of a
follower building on his shoulders. None of these men
is Debussy taking Moussorgsky and "Parsifal" and making something new with them. Part of each is seated
among the men who are indeed creating new sounds; part
of each is individual among the individualities whom we
respect and admire and wait upon for significant experiments, and rejoice in having. But part of each one is
unfree and undetermined and following childishly in the
paths other men have cut for themselves.

Three of the men, Alfredo Casella, Ildebrando Pizzetti
and G. Francesco Malipiero stand distinguished by the
seriousness of their gifts; and in the flow of all three
there are traces of an unclarity. Casella, for example,
is brilliant but dry. The wells beneath are not sending
their wet up through him. He has the keenest sense of
what is in progress in musical art; he never strikes orchestra or pianoforte but the medium becomes awake with
crispness and acrid new sounds; he is among the boldest
of musicians, harmonically and rhythmically; an intelligence at the very forefront of musical culture. And yet
his work is somehow a little unsatisfactory and smelling
always a little of the lamp. His cerebralism is never so
patent as when, as in the rhapsody "Italia," he seeks to be
vulgar and earthy, and, being an Italian, thoroughly spa-
ghetti. The orchestra may seek to strike the bardic strain
and later gurgle and burble with popular joy; the hand
of the artifex makes itself felt in the thinness of the
piece.

Did Casella harmonize an occasional passage in consecutive fourths, one might accept the trick as an earmark
of a certain sort of feeling. But, before a man who persists in harmonizing everything in consecutive fourths

willy-nilly, one commences to suspect a definite apriorism
and cerebral interference. It is as one who cannot permit
life to approach him nakedly and directly, that one sees
this genial and interesting musician. The impulse does
not come sufficiently from below, through feeling. It
seems to come transmitted through the air to the Eiffel
tower of his mind; there to be deciphered and analyzed
and prepared for future use. He sees what Strawinsky
and Ravel and Schoenberg are about; appreciates their
work with nicety; but when he sits down freighted with
an idea, the foreigners mix themselves in unbeknownst,
and conduct the process. Sometimes, Casella comes very
near working in the living substance; the pieces for two
pianos called "Puppazetti" dance with their own life; the
"Notte di Maggio" has dignity and weight. "A notte alto"
has a distinctive frosty coloration; and the two of the
"Nove Pezze" called "In modo di populo" and "In modo di
barbaro" have real and Strawinsky-like rhythmical life.
Nevertheless, the man is too much brilliant star-dust
afloat between the cosmopolitan centers. He parches us
for want of some fluid which many a less adventuresome
harmonist possesses, and which the mind alone does not
secrete.

Pizzetti is more earthfast; and his music in its relative
freshness confesses itself the outgrowth of feeling. His
sonata for violin and piano is a most sincere and dignified
work; the music of a man who goes toward instruments
because he has to speak a woe and passion within. Pizzetti is the descendant of the old Tuscan aristocracy, and
his fine nature seems to bring into modern music something of the racial musical gift in its soberest and noblest
state. There are moments when he makes one to think
of a modern Corelli; the crying lamenting cutting tones
of the fiddle in his violin and piano sonata; the dramatic

almost gesticulating passion have the simplicity, directness, and robustness of the great seventeenth century
Italian. Nevertheless, Pizzetti is far less tonally advanced than is Casella, and than is the Venetian Malipiero. He goes very little beyond César Franck; and his
harmonies are generally quite simple. That in itself would
be no cardinal disadvantage, were Pizzetti always and not
merely often, the aristocrat, the chaste and distinguished
nature in music. He might be a sort of Brahms of Italian
art. Unfortunately, he has his melancholy lapses. If, in
distinction to Casella and Malipiero, he has resisted all
foreign allurements, and remained always Italian, he permits himself from time to time to be sucked into Charybdis. He agitates the racial rhetoric. The middle movement of the sonata, the "Preghiera per gl'innocenti" descends into some very broad Puccini. Again Floria Tosca
warbles "Vissi d'arte, vissi d'amore" while Scarpia cracks
peanut shells and prepares a rape.

With Malipiero, Italy throws nearest the ranks of the
important ultramoderns. Of the three most interesting
of the newer men, the Venetian is the one vested most with
the appearance of genius. What he gives forth is vibrant;
quick with some electric fluid which arrests the pulse.
His music is rich with his living sense of new and daring
sonorities. Some of his little piano-sketches he has called
"Rissonanze"; the name fits what is most immediately
attractive in all his music. The dissonances of the bell
tones in the "Colloquio di campane" of the second set of
"Impressioni dal vero"; the moment in the "Grottesco"
when the piccolo shrills above the sudden descent and
black rumble of the piano's tones; the light strumming
of the fiddles in the string quartet, mark him one of the
foremost of living colorists. There is a young brilliance
in much of his work. The grotesque has really clownish

rhythm. There is the haggard gray of the hour of war-parting in "I partenti" in the "Poemi Asolani," with its plangent steely tones and frenetic excitement cast into a single hurrying form. One feels the true musician in this recapture of a terrible and unforgettable moment. And the choral work "Saint Francis of Assisi" has some of the great simple poignancy and tenderness we associate with Moussorgsky. The very stuff of poesy is obviously here. But Malipiero seems still to be in a state of inner indecision. One cannot feel he has as yet found himself. There is an Italian largeness and directness in him; but as Pizzetti in the Charybdis of racial insensitivity, so Malipiero comes to grief on the Scylla of derivative idiom. At moments, as in the "Impressioni dal vero," he recalls the "Miroirs" of Ravel; at others, as in the "Grottesco" —in "Barlumi" and in "Rispetti e Strombotti," Strawinsky of "Petrushka" and the "Sacre." Besides, there is something unorganized and sometimes nearly chaotic in his more extended forms. The string-quartet, for example, is dead several minutes before the composer concludes. Nor is his manner of writing always happy. We find him at the selfsame trick at which we have discovered Scott. He shifts his beat very often, contrasting five fourths with four, and five sixths with two thirds; but with some of the same lack of persuasiveness with which Scott makes the same maneuver. Both composers seem bent on varying the extent of their phrases whether the variation is natural or no.

And yet, scarcely a geographical musical division holds our interest more intensely than does that occupied by these newcomers. Particularly for men in America has the experiment in progress in Italy a unique significance. There is a great similarity between the conditions which Casella and his group have to meet and those which oppose our own musicians. The Italians are somewhat more advanced in technique and in style than are the Americans. But the situation in which musical creation finds itself in the peninsula is essentially the same in which it finds itself in our own land. We, too, are sophisticated; unrooted in our own community; living half by a European culture and half by a middle class barbarism, and existing in the emotional poverty flowing from the state of division. We, too, look toward France and behold there in an interpenetrated, integrated society an object of whole-hearted envy; the community wherein one does not have, whatever the amount of one's strength, to hold up the wall of faith with one hand while with the other, one hastily tries to do. And so we peel our eyes towards Italy, and watch, as the inhabitants of Earth might watch the canals on Mars: in the hope of a greater clarification of our own problem.

January, 1921.

"*Louise*"

I⊤ is as long gone as are the days when they gave opera in New York City, that the "Louise" of Charpentier was first presented here, and the intervening years have not warred quite lightly against the score. At the time when Oscar Hammerstein mounted the musical romance, it was as heady as champagne. It came over one with all the intoxication which must have been communicated by the painting of the impressionists when first it was shown the world. For, like this picturing of the endless variety of the moment, it seemed to throw open a secret door upon some common throbbing immediacy, and let one out of the cloudlands of the ideal onto some street of to-day. Like "Tristan," it called to a sensual fulfillment; but it called to a fulfillment far easier of attainment than did the high song of bodily love.

This headiness it has lost. To-day, even though it still tastes sweet, it wants the sparkle and foaminess and potency it had, or seemed to have. The score has not the depth and abundance which carries the fullness of the composer's intention across the spaces of time. It is far thinner than one remembered it to be; sentimental and Massenet-like, even, in places. Although the work is what many operas are not, the fleshing of a conception, the definition of a floating feeling, the musical inventions which fix this inner conception are neither very strong, very distinguished, nor greatly varied. Charpentier's foothold is a very precarious one. The fine bits, the music that accompanies the drinking of the soup in Act I, the

114

street cries and sewing-machine music in Act II, arrest momentarily a flow always a little too easy. The valse movement is repeated so often that already in the third act one is irritated at its reappearance; the Paris music of the final scene veritably requires the melodramatic stage-business to save its effectiveness, so over-familiar does it become through the constant service to which the composer puts it.

And still, despite the sheerness, the music remains sufficiently stout to bear incontrovertible witness to one fact, the one fact to which it has hitherto always testified. Even in the form of a revival by the Metropolitan Opera House, even in the form of revival typical of the Metropolitan Opera House, with Geraldine obscuring the title rôle, the stage set as though Gordon Craig had never lived, and sincerity quite wanting to the performance, the score of "Louise" still attests that its author felt Paris, felt its quiver of life with the sensitiveness of a lover.

Whether it was the love of the city that made him love its little shop-girls; or whether it was the love for the midinette that made him love the air she breathed, the streets she walked, we do not know. All Charpentier tells us, in the words spoken by Julien to his sweetheart, is that "Hors Paris, Louise ne serait Louise! Paris, sans toi, ne serait pas Paris." We can only guess the two feelings grew together, and augmented one another, till the musician came to feel in the city the woman, and in the pleasure-mad child of the luminous town, the spreading city-world again. But, what it was he felt about both, that the score makes manifest. The opera is not a piece of stage-business; a mere outer show; a dressing of actor-singers in blouses and shirtwaists; an exhibition on the operatic stage, where most usually only gods and diademed kings, and folk in exotic and medieval costume

walk, of three workpeople eating cabbage soup about a
kerosene lamp. It is an idea. The music catches indeed
some of the quality, the movement, of the *gens du peuple*.
It uses popular rhythms, popular tones; takes up into
itself some of the accent of popular expression. It has
some of the quality of the drag-skirted Parisian boule-
vard crowds; some of the quality of the people of the
bals; some of the vulgar grace of the trim, greedy-sensual
little midinettes, with their sugary voluptuousness. One
hears the streets; the cries of the water-cress sellers, of
the hawkers along the faubourgs; the whirring of sewing
machines in dress-making ateliers. The bath of sentimentality which flows about these islets does not spoil
them for us. The moments of light poetry come again;
and we smell life. We feel the family of Parisian
laborers sitting down at close of day to eat their bread
and stew and drink their *ordinaire*. We feel the little
workgirls sitting in their workroom above the fashionable
street dreaming of luxury and lovers and satiety; the hour
of dusk when the lamps on the great thoroughfares lend a
sort of magic to the world, and a city of bricks of light
flows down and away from the *Butte*.

For all his thinness and tawdriness, Charpentier has
caught something almost universal in his music. He has
managed to get into his score a little of the glamor which
the capital on the Seine has for every one, for Parisians,
provincials, and outlanders alike. The fanfares of mystic
trumpets, brutal and brilliant, which the American hears
when the name of Lutetia Parisiorum enters his consciousness; the waltz of the blood, the sharp tattoos, the
laughter of pleasure-drunken crowds, which are Paris to
him whether he be desolate in Syracuse, New York, or in
Peoria, Illinois, or standing pensive beside the pensive
gargoyle of Notre Dame, are in "Louise." The music

speaks pleasure, a curious blend of pleasure and luxury, of love and dinners at intimate restaurants, of passion and fireworks. The flesh sings cunningly, softly; a little dream, a little sensuality, a little longing, a little gourmandise, wake, and honey the blood. We see the flank of the Louvre and hear the band at the bal Bullier, remember the moonlit Bois and the liqueurs on the café tables, the melancholy of the waterworks at Versailles, and the crispness of the *pommes souflées* at the restaurant Laperouse. Suddenly, we recollect that liners sail almost daily for Cherbourg. Within ten days, one might be on the rue de Rivoli! What price transportation?

And since "Louise" has demonstrated its power to resist not only Metropolitan Opera House singers and Metropolitan Opera managers, but the Metropolitan Opera House audience which encourages singers and managers in their odious habits, and is responsible chiefly for the morgue-like chill that has settled, permanently it appears, upon the noble old theatre in Thirty-ninth Street, who can doubt the durability of the work? It has resisted that terrible audience wanting imagination, wanting sympathy for the composer; and awaiting, with greatest eagerness, the moments when the lights flare up for the entr'acte, and the performance which it came to see will indeed commence; and the old ladies shrouded in ermine capes leave their seats to walk up one aisle and down the other. It has resisted the people without respect for their neighbors, willing to mar the whole of the first act of every opera by trailing in tardily all through it and slamming down seats, willing to mar the last by trailing out again in order not to have to wait too long for automobiles, ready to disturb their entire entourage by conversations in stage whispers carried on during the performance (oh, these inevitable conversations that commence just as the prelude to, say, "Tristan" begins its anguished confession, oh, those ubiquitous dames who manage, just as the orchestra begins speaking to remember something of flaming importance that must be said immediately, and cannot bear postponement, that must be said immediately lest worlds go under). Since, then, "Louise" has demonstrated itself a match for neurotic America and its thousand coughs, who shall dare affirm that generations will not know it much as we know it now? It appears probable that when men come to speak of the poets who, during the nineteenth century, expressed the excitement of great cities, they will speak of Balzac; they will speak of Whitman; they will speak of D'Annunzio and his descriptions of modern Rome in "Il Piacere," of Venice in "Il Fuoco"; and they will not, before the list is completed, forget entirely the name of Charpentier and his "Louise."

February, 1921.

Concerts at the Museum

THE orchestra was invisible at the free concerts conducted by David Mannes Saturday evenings in January and March at the Metropolitan Museum of Art. It was placed up in the north end of the gallery which overhangs the great stone entrance hall; and only the sounds themselves indicated its position. The remainder of the gallery, the floor of the tapestried hall, the broad staircase at the foot of which floats upward the green bronze boy of Rodin were given over to the audience. People were permitted to comport themselves much as they would; to walk, to sit, to stand, to lean, to listen to the music in any position preferred by them. The museum was lit throughout; and if they wanted, folk could wander from the music into the tranquil illuminated rooms hung with the canvases and set with the statuary. A restraining hand had been laid upon the guards. When some one peered into a glass case, stentorian commands did not shatter the spell of art. Detective-like glances fraught with the terrible blinding suspicion that here at last was the man who was going to cut the Rembrandt out of its gilt frame, did not pursue visitors who stepped close to works for the purpose of examining them detailedly. Babylon the Great, in the guise of blue-tunic'd attendants, was fallen, was fallen; and reduced to gently making aisles for promenaders.

There was a pleasant ease and naturalness pervading the place. People sat at the bases of sarcophagi. People rested their backs and necks against granite Egyptian deities. People stood, their heads lifted or depressed.

their overcoat collars up or open, while the tones from the gallery broadened and fell. The crowd circulated slowly, quietly; sat on grass-mats in the staircase. One saw families standing grouped. A pair of lovers sat close and lost on the steps. There were women with babies in their arms. An invalid was wheeled about in a bath-chair. A child sucked at the nipple of a bottle. Against a fish-shaped Egyptian sculpture there crouched, her bobbed head ecstatically upturned, a girl with high forehead and bold protruding modern features. Another, coquettish in a trim dolman, dreamily leaned her elbow at the foot of "L'age d'airain," and hearkened to the sounds of the "Siegfried Idyll" that throbbed through the great filled place.

And music was again become a simple and nourishing thing, an integral part of life. Music was again a thing like nutrition and love, like sickness and age, a portion of the natural process. Not even the fact that the performance was not a very fine one, the program routine, the brasses uncertain, detracted from the vitality of the experience. The sick cast which the concert hall gives the performances of music; the sense of guilt for time wasted and misused in personal indulgence which it manages to introduce even into the pleasure imparted, was absent. One did not feel ashamed of being there; of surfeiting oneself weakly with candy when one might be out on the street seeing building shapes and cloud-ramparts and faces of passing people; or reading a book; or writing a letter. One did not have the sense that listening to these tones, most of which one had heard before, was something at which it would have been embarassing to be caught. These concerts brought release. One heard music again, received it like the breath of health. The hearing of it was again become a worthy and an important function, close to the bone.

Music itself had been released. In performers and audience alike there had been permitted to erect itself something of the same spirit which expressed itself in the making of beautiful song, some of the same self-forgetful feeling for the flowering element in the universe. There was no exhibition of *virtuosi* by means of art. The orchestra was hidden from the greater portion of the audience. Music was given in a spirit of self-effacement before beauty. No performer trod before the gathering and bade it observe him swell his bosom or wave his arms. No virtuoso used music to glorify his soul. Nor was music used for the purpose of exhibiting a gathering. There were no boxes, no orchestra-stalls, no galleries. There was no preening of bedizened gargoyles, no ostrich fans, airs of painful distinction, brilliant conversational attitudes vis-à-vis the auditorium, ermine capes; no self-awareness of the audience.

The music went out from the instruments in the spirit in which it had been imparted to them by the composer: as a gift to every one and all who wanted to receive it. No admission fee was demanded. It was there for those who needed to hear it. Nothing was demanded of these save that they receive it in the way it was offered. And it went out to folk under circumstances that did not remove them from their thoughts, their ordinary lives, the actual world in which they earned their bread and begot children and whistled and wept. It went to them in such a way that would bring them deeper into their thoughts, deeper into themselves, closer to what was going on about them in the customary walks. The museum those nights did not interrupt, as does the concert-hall, the style of life. The face of the world was all about one. True, any place of ordinary concourse would have served the purpose as well and perhaps better than the museum. This

was a makeshift, merely. Nevertheless, the desired effect
was produced in it; for it was permitted, during the hours
the band discoursed there, to take on the character of a
spot of ordinary concourse, in which folk might come
direct from their toil, with their families and friends, and
live and visit as they did when they were most natural.
Amid all these forms of existence, amid the babies and
the invalids, the lovers and the family men, the uncon-
strained attitudes of the human frames and sculptures,
the rough modern fabrics and antique basalts, nursing-
bottles and wheel-chairs, bobbed hair and wakening
women, one was in the center of New York and of the
world, the ancient and the modern. And music floated
one further in.

But, chiefest among the causes of the genuineness of
the experience was the fact that one shared the music
with people. During those hours, one was single in purpose with men and women. The best of life was coming
to one together with people. One was not, as in the
concert-hall, even when it is most jammed, separate from
people. Here no property distinction existed. One was
part of ordinary humanity, part of the crowd which is not
removed from the fundamentals of existence; and yet
one was receiving with them the finest honey of the
spirit. One was a member of that great community which
trembles a dazzling vision over the highest moments of
dream; the community in the soul. So music winged its
way. For it is to men as members in that great community that it addresses itself. It is of music as well as
of joy that Schiller might have sung:

> Deine Zauber binden wieder,
> Was die Mode streng geteilt.

It comes from a human being to human beings; from a brother to brethren.

> Alle Menschen werden Brüder
> Wo dein sanfter Flügel weilt.

March, 1921.

Szymanowski

THERE is a poem of Hubert Trench's which pictures an Apollo "in furred raiment" entering an English tavern and sitting at meat with mariners. Unintentionally, certain compositions of Karol Szymanowski make one to imagine similar and equally charming transmogrifications. When the young Polish composer arrived here, one of a brilliant trio of comets about to traverse the musical system of New York and return and disappear eastward again, he carried with him several recently completed works, a sonata and three "Masques" for piano solo, several songs, and three "Myths" for piano and violin; these last, "La fontaine d'Arethuse," "Narcisse" and "Pan et Dryade" are the compositions which particularly evoke the figures of demigods become septentrional and quaintly transformed. The world which the duo of instruments enchants before us is not the world of flooding dayshine and dry warmth in which the animal deities of Greece are usually seen disporting themselves. The capricious cascades of the elegant music make one to feel himself far from the light and heat of Mediterranean shores. It is to a northern clime of short days and long winters they transport. A benign and comfortable atmosphere bathes one still; but it is the atmosphere of the *salon* of a great Polish manor-house, a manor, say, somewhere without the gates of Warsaw; and the calorification comes less directly from the sun than from the porcelain stove. The writhing movements of the dryad struggling in the arms of the god, the passionate unhappy efforts of Narcissus to embrace the unsubstantial image mirrored before him, appear to be made in a room furnished with brocaded armchairs, mirror-borders of faded gilt, crucifixi and portraits of periwigged dignitaries of Poniatowski's reign; and giving through long windows on a snowy terrace under heavy skies. Arethusa, without a doubt, is a Comtesse, lovely, perhaps, as the perennial Potocka; a gracile head tantalizing with little curls. Narcissus is certainly a highborn composer of soft delightful manners; a scion of the race of Chopin, and pupil to Moritz Moskowski. And the goat-hoofed god unquestionably is a *pan;* the dryad has yellow braids and goes to confession; and it is by the light-points of wax candles sconced in a chandelier that she is clutched and overwhelmed.

Szymanowski is a brilliant, an exquisitely refined, and an anæmic talent. His work is delicate, full of the ineffable Slavonic grace, bold in harmonic feeling and concise in form; and oblique, cool, and wanting in directness and warm vibrancy. It is an iridescent and polished surface, truly distinguished and fine, but without body and nourishing passion. The piercing harmonies and acidulous colors and brute masses of the newest music are become, under this dainty and forceless hand, a little wan and noble and charmingly weak. Ravel is recalled at moments by the blandness of sound and the distinction of manner of Szymanowski's compositions. And yet beside this chlorotic northern music Ravel's seems warm and dense and animal even. They are part of to-day, these sonatas and songs, symphonies and poems, for the composer has genuinely original ideas. But they are the world approached so indirectly, so obliquely; felt through so thick a curtain of formality and preconceived and even pedantic ideas, that the beat of things comes through them muffled and cotton-wooled. The music is of the drawing-room, even though it remains sincere and noble. Something has limited it overmuch to functioning as a brilliant amusement, a glitter and sparkle which touches lightly the surface of life, and stirs no painful depths. It is neither cynical nor brutal; it makes a reverence before the heart and says "I perfectly perceive, my lord, that you are regent; I recognize the supreme wonder and terribleness of your way." But in so doing, it denies and disposes of the guilty organ cavalierly. It touches only the ghost of the rose.

Szymanowski is the seraphic teaser among the ultramoderns. Some quality of life, sensitive in itself, is not carried fully through. The dislocation is apparent, in many of his works, in the contrast furnished by the color-effect and the musical design onto which it is grafted. For whilst the one is generally of a fabulous daintiness, the other, especially in the larger forms, is sometimes no more than the purely intellectual working out of the thematic material. Szymanowski is a brilliant and a rare colorist; the three "Myths," for example, make one to hear the violin anew. He has used, it seems, the virtuosity of his friend, Paul Kochanski, constructively. This violinist, who is indeed not so much a violinist as an artist, has invented a novel way of playing his instrument. He can play harmonics with the utmost facility. His subtlety on the instrument is so great that one gets veritable pleasure from listening to the timbres of what is usually little more than the whining moron of the band. Profiting by Kochanski's gift Szymanowski has written three poems that make one to forget completely the old odious habits of the violin. His musical texture, to quote from a sympathetic Polish commentator, is full of "fantastic harmonics, an inexhaustible variety of spiccatos, of chords and double stoppings." The strings tinkle and shine. In

"Narcisse," the best of the pieces, cascades of silvery bubbles foam. All three are full of capricious, mandolin-like music, cool, melancholy and pricking. Some of the selfsame delicate instrumental virtuosity, transferred onto other instruments of the band, gives the ballet-music written by Szymanowski for "Le Bourgeois Gentil-homme" its value. For if the musical design, with its quotation of Lulli, remains only very tamely humorous, the instruments themselves realize veritable comedy. And in his recent piano-music, the composer masters a style less dazzling perhaps than his writing for the violin, but nevertheless light and firm. The third sonata with its fantastic fugue-theme, "scherzando e buffo," which resembles the shrilling of some dream-cockatoo, is almost Chopinesque in the happy and elegant disposition of the material, the pianistic hardness and richness.

Once you abandon this sensuous and most attractive surface, once you look on the matter proper, your finds become of more doubtful value. Szymanowski is very uncertain in his selection of thematic stuff. He has a characteristic and delicate vein of ideas; the graceful, coquettish, Slavic theme of the variations of the a-major sonata, the light staccato second subject of the sonata number three and the hopping theme of the fugue, express his elegant nature in its truer aspect. Yet, by the side of these aristocratic and original motifs, in the selfsame works in which they figure, he places material of a complexion distinctly not his own. Certain of these compositions remind one of a spiritual map of Poland. For mixed in with some genuine green there appears not only the sere past, but vast regions of German, Russian, and French influence. The sarabande of the a-major sonata is heavily Franckian. The initial theme of the third calls to mind a much diluted Chopin. In the vainglorious first movement of the b-major symphony, Szymanowski's solitary and not very successful attempt to speak the language of the sort of martial, boastful Pole which he, the gentle Pole, is not, the names of Strauss and Scriabine are used to conjure with. A kind of etiolated "Tristan" sounds its pale passion in the three "Masques" for piano.

It seems that while Szymanowski does feel, he feels only in spurts, and not with his whole man. Preconceived ideas appear with ease to invade his mind while it is in labor, to topple over the edifices life is raising in him, and erect themselves in life's despite. There are always large pieces of intellectualization in the forms of his longer compositions. Even in the third sonata, which represents Szymanowski's harmonic sense at its boldest, spots of truly Germanic pedantry obtrude. After the first statement of the winged second subject, *animato, leggiero e grazioso,* there occurs a passage in minor thirds which recalls Max Reger at his most crabbed moments. The connecting passages of the fugue consist of equally formal and mechanical working out of the music, and move with the port of something which they are not indeed. Not even the many passages of brilliant music, the final page with its exquisite blending of themes, its joyous coda, for example, can quite erase the sense of chill and of poverty amid riches communicated by the empty spots.

For the reason perhaps that the program frees him of some of his classical obsessions, Szymanowski's essays in descriptive music are the hardest and wholest of his compositions for instruments. They leave us less conscious than do some of the others of his limitations. The three "Masques" for piano, "Scheherazade," "Tantris der Narr," and "Eine Don Juan Serenade," with all the Tristanesque lyricism, have a pleasing directness and dramatic intensity. Each of these pieces contrasts two moods. And the interplay of the two subjects, the one ostentatious and protective, the other secret and repressed, is managed with considerable cleverness. Scheherazade, full of the fear of impending death, forces herself into making brilliant and intriguing gestures, into whipping her emotions to dazzling pitch, for the purpose of charming her tyrant into forgetfulness. But underneath the apparent animation and passion and intoxication the old gnawing terror lurks, and returns constantly upon her. "Tantris der Narr," true to the motif of the drama of Ernst Hardt, interweaves in similar fashion the loud laughter of the pretended zany, the rattling of his bells, the harebrained talk, and the terrible surging of the emotion of love which threatens at every moment to tear from his face the mask. And Don Juan, the man who fares distractedly through the world in vain search for the woman who will thaw open his frozen breast, and turns disappointed and untouched from each new conquest, twangs his mandolin in pretended frenzy, tries to augment his cleverly assumed passion, proffers fiery declaration upon declaration; but, the immediate object attained, slinks away again disgruntled and wearied and bored.

Of all his compositions it is perhaps some of his songs which make one to feel the real charm of his mind most purely. Szymanowski has the power to create instantaneously a mood; and where no further demand than that of such a brief creation is made of his talent, he emerges with standard erect. Some of his earlier songs, "Bunte Lieder" and the setting of the six lyrics of Hafiz, show him still in quest of a personal manner. But in the setting of Tagore's poems, and in the group which includes "St. François" and "Feu de joie," Szymanowski has given us some of the most exquisite and original of modern songs; and the essence of his infinitely sensitive and delicate musicianship. The latter group recalls somewhat the three myths for violin, the attenuated, pastellike, bubbling, Slavonically graceful music built out of the white tones of the instrument. In these whiffs of song, too, we find the composer moving in the compass of what is oblique and unusual and remote in the soprano voice. The voice sings falsetto, sings high in the head, over the delicate dissonant filigree of the piano accompaniment. Tones that are more boy and old man than woman strain from the feminine larynx. Nevertheless, the songs are as nuggets of purest gold compared to the elaborately chased silver of the violin music. They seem to come from deep within the composer, and to carry the ecstasies of a shy, proud, reserved nature. All the seraphic delicacy which is spread so thinly over other of his works is in them collected and expressed in a few glistening periods of music. They both convince us beyond every doubt of the uniqueness of the composer's talent, and serve to make us the more dissatisfied with the greater amount of what he has given thus far.

March, 1921.

The Bloch Violin Sonata

ERNEST BLOCH'S sonata for violin and piano calls to mind certain pages of "La Tentation de Saint Antoine." It calls to mind the adamantine page where the devil slings the saint upon his horns, and carries him out into the empyrean amid the planets, and makes him to perceive the infinitude of matter; thought encased in matter; and matter higher than sight however high one lifts one's eyes. It calls to mind also the final scene, where the monstrous animality of the earth becomes visible to the delirious dreamer, and he imagines himself viewing the origin of life. For in Bloch's music, too, we come to perceive, with impersonal eye, the titanic, virulent and incommensurable forces upon whose breast man lies tiny and impotent. We are as though placed on a platform somewhere without the universe, and nevertheless permitted to see ourselves in the grasp of the natural powers, spurned about as a football. In the roaring of the piano and the impersonal singing of the violin, we feel nature, nature before man, nature which is grandly impervious to man and his woe, nature which tramples ruthlessly upon him, and drowns his wailing in her unending storm. Forces are seen fighting each other through man, fighting over his body, trampling his carcass as heavily as the cruel crowned and wingèd bulls graved on the palace-walls of Nineveh might trample. Forces hurl his petty edifices to the ground, pass onward majestic and indifferent, obedient to the ineluctable law. We watch the grandiose comedy from afar, yet all the

while feel the blows that fall as fall stones shot into the
air by blasting. We feel the sharpness and hardness
and coldness of cliffs on which no life can persist. We
are shaken till there is no breath left in us. We are cast
aside like withered pods, while the fury sweeps away
from us into regions of the skies.

The three movements of the sonata develop three
facets of the central idea. If, in the first, the piano
seizes us in its talons, and carries us breathless aloft
into the whirlwind, and makes us feel in the very flesh
the beat of earthly power, the second shows us no less
an elemental force, even though it makes us to view
it in a slower, more lethargic, more somnolent manifes-
tation. The movement seems to show us nature at her
work of generation; to represent the blind dumb impulse
that drives life in the spring, and softly, imperiously,
bends the organism to do its will. Strange love-music
indeed, this middle section of the Bloch sonata! We
have gone far, since Wagner wrote the prelude to
"Tristan"! There, it was still the oceanic tide of human
desire that swelled and fell and swelled again. Here,
the music brings to mind not man, but swarming and
surging microscopic organisms, innumerable billions of
bacteria. High on the piano and violin there commences
a creeping sing-song, a shimmering restless theme that
slowly, waveringly, descends and gathers strength, in-
creases till the thin trickle grows into a stream. Heat,
heat of the swamps in which animal life first grew,
steams upward. Then, as though sluice-gates had
slowly been opened till they stood wide, the floods pour
forth; pour forth uncontrollably, copiously, darkly, a
monstrous torrent.

A brief scherzando passage interposes itself; the harmonics of the violin give off sparks of color. But even

this passage is inhuman; it makes us to see merely the dance of insects during the mating-season, the glimmer of swamp lights in tropic darkness. And once again, the great relentless floods begin to rise, to tower to even greater heights than before; then, like an immense heaven-storming breaker, to curl over, and collapse and inundate the world. The strength of innumerable lives seems to be spilled with indifferent, dull liberality. Nature seems to take the whole of her creations' life, and with cruel relentless force press it out that her ends may be served. With the same slow, somnolent movement with which the section began, the music of heat and of swarming, germinating animal life decreases, fails, and dies away.

Once again, in the third movement, we are shown the "trampling march of unconscious power." But there is a distinction between the last and the other two movements, greater than the distinction between the first and second. In the two earlier sections, we ourselves were still somewhat implicated in the action; there are violin phrases, particularly in the allegro, that are the plaints of the human cockle-shell tossed on oceanic tides. But the last section seems to dissociate us entirely from the clatter and the fury; we seem to be without it completely, and regarding it with wholly objective eye. Like some gaudy and meaningless pageant in the skies, some play of garish fires, the battle of creation moves before us. With elephantine tread, life, like a bloody conqueror marching over the corpses of his countless victims, prances onward, all dirt and blood and triumph. There is no glory in this music, only massive, savage march-rhythm; no splendor—only the pompousness of something beefy and horribly abundant. The whole of heaven seems to reverberate with the clatter of the victor

as he mounts to take possession of his inheritance. Only
as the pageant dwindles in the unplumbed spaces of the
universe, does something that is recognizable as human
speech begin to take possession of the music, and come
to the fore. The last movement ends with a tranquil
passage that serves as epilogue to the entire work. The
quiet flowing of piano and violin are like the words of
one who has faced completely the nature of life, who has
seen it for the shamble that it is, and who holds himself,
not in weak despair, not in lachrymose resignation, but
in a sort of stoical steadfastness. The tones communicate, not bitterness, not scorn or self-pity, but only a sort
of iron disillusioned acceptance; stern submission to the
inevitable.

Flaubert was not the first man to front life with such
an expression of face, and Ernest Bloch will not be the
last who will do so. Still, this violin sonata is exquisitely
timely. It brings a gift to this very day. Its composer
is one of those few men who give life to their spirit
through the the composition of music and hence give
life to those in whom the spirit struggles, too. The piece
seems to us the deed by which a man freed his lungs
to greater capacity in the smoky air of the world that
saw the war, that bore the heaven-storming piles of the
American cities, that has seen and heard the immense
aggregation of human beings in the giant towns, the falling together of many races, the shrilling of many tongues.
Bloch has done many deeds of the sort. The composition of the "Three Psalms" comes to us as the act whereby
he won for himself manly pride, the sense of the right
of his two feet to the earth, the liberty of drawing his
breath in joy, which life had long refused him in making
him the child of a race without a land, a Jew living
among alien-speaking peoples. A world-wide movement

could know itself in the accents of the proud chants. The composition of "Schelomo" comes to us as the act by means of which he rid himself of resentments born of his personal fate. And in making the sonata for piano and violin, Bloch seems to have been about conquering his own terrible tenderness; about finding within himself the firmness and toughness of spirit capable of facing life as the peace showed it; and of fulfilling itself careless of personal success and failure. He had found himself with all the rest of humankind conscious of the utter helplessness of the individual man; conscious of the horrid forces within the human breast with which the paltry human intelligence has to contend; conscious of what beautiful man with his thirst for the ideal is everlastingly doing to his fellow, and to himself. He had found himself, with all the rest of humankind, alone. And then, slowly, from day to day, there had come to wax in him a sort of growl of defiance, a sort of savage chanting of the thought, "Lay on, Macduff!", a leaping sensation of a strength that could not be defeated, since loss of personal life brought no defeat with it; until at last a piece of music was inside him like a six-months' child in the womb; and the impulse strong to shout into the maw of heaven the truth.

In what manner the sounds of a stringed instrument and of an instrument of percussion can signify such spiritual currents to a roomful of auditors, and send steel through brittle bones; in what manner an order superimposed upon nature's chaos can come to represent that chaos, one can only dumbly guess. Communication through material form remains as ineluctable a mystery as the mystery of personality itself; and an examination of the surface of the music grants us the vaguest hints, only. No doubt, the musical design offers a number of

clews to the origins of the grandiose images projected by
the performance in the minds of so many of the audience. There is little reason to doubt that the immense
rhythmic and harmonic freedom of the music, the absence
of tenderness and sentimentality, the directness, helps
make it seem elemental. Bloch's rhythms have become
increasingly ferocious, abrupt, far-flung; they mutate
incessantly, so much as to make the rhythmic element
of the works of his second period, the "Hebraic" period,
appear regular and limited. Tonality has long since dis-
appeared from modern music, but the passages in the
Bloch sonata, where the two instruments play at the
same time in two distinct keys, give us new ears indeed.
The melodic line, again, rugose, melancholy, capricious,
alternates between wild emphasis and subtle shadings.
The highest and lowest registers of both instruments are
used continuously; the violin pours a tanny savage color
over the work. And then, the dynamics of the two instruments are brought into play by the composition with
extraordinary freedom. The effects the composer obtains
upon piano and violin are grandly orchestral. They are
so orchestral that, at the première, one heard angry
voices inquiring the reason he had not turned directly
to the band to express himself. Since, however, Bloch
had shown that he could do the thing with the aid of
only two performers; since Messrs. Arthur Rubenstein
and Paul Kochanski presented the work as powerfully,
sympathetically, and perfectly as any work of Bloch's
has ever been presented, the question remains a piece of
unthinkingness.

It is in the terrific energy of movement, the grandiose
pressure of vitality, which the sonata records, that we
find the general factor responsible for the effect the music
had. The energy which has hurled his compositions

forth from him has long set Ernest Bloch apart among
living musicians. There is no one of them who encloses
as great a tension in the body of his music as this
Genevan. There is no one who suspends such piles of
stone and steel across the gulfs of time as lightly as he.
"Schelomo," the quartet, the violin sonata, have this kinship with the mighty works of Beethoven, and with "Tristan" and "Die Walküre": that in them too we feel the im-
press of an entire man. We feel a man giving himself
completely, in all the tension of his swollen muscles, in
all the weight and hotness of his blood, pressing the last
inch of his life into his work so that nothing can be left
within him, so that death if it comes to-morrow will find
itself cheated of its spoils. Others among living composers excel Bloch in fecundity of invention. His thematic material is not always the most distinguished; the
divine oboe theme of "Schelomo" does not find compeers
in every work he writes. He has neither the rhythmic
invention of Strawinsky, nor the harmonic subtlety of
Schoenberg. Some of the motifs of the sonata, like that
of the scherzo proper of the quartet, verge on the usual.
But what Bloch succeeds in doing with his stuff, makes
it an unusual thing. He has a power of living development, of sustainment and replenishment, which is almost
Beethoven-like in its breadth. No one among the ultramoderns, not even Scriabine, can in any sense rival this
man in his gift of bringing out the unexpected within the
limits of the given; of finding a second breath immediately upon the giving out of the first, and a third immediately on the failing of the second, and carrying
onward his material to new births and forms. The fall,
the break, for which one waits so often in many new
things, does not come, in Bloch. The music rides on.
The line remains fluid, stiff, and unbroken. And were

it not for the richness of the curves and the nuances, one might compare its movement to the even bowling of a railroad train.

It is as yet too early to predict the rank the sonata will assume among Bloch's compositions. Its characteristics place it immediately among the works of his "third period"; for, like the quartet and the suite, the two compositions which immediately preceded it, its accents and coloration are somewhat less racial and Biblical than those of the "Psalms," of the "Trois Poèmes Juifs," and of the 'cello rhapsody. Its language is oriental and barbaric, primitive, more than Semitic and Hebrew. But the acquaintanceship we have with the music is too brief to permit us to attempt any deeper appreciation, to permit us to judge whether it represents as great a maturity of inspiration as of force. And yet, we know this: that whatever the rank it finally assumes, that of a masterpiece of a great musician, or that of a work of smaller significance, it can never stand before us in any other aspect than that of a piece of music of the first importance. We owe to it a musical experience of an intensity which does not arrive very often in life. We owe to it a feeling of an intensity which we can only compare to those aroused in us by the first hearing of "Die Meistersinger," of "Pelléas," of the "Sacre." We owe to it a confidence in our own time, in its color and its power, second to that given us by no piece of music.

March, 1921.

All-Tchaikowsky Program

'Twas in the musical red-light district that the series of performances given by the Philadelphia Orchestra in New York during the season of 1920-1921 ended. All-Tchaikowsky was the program tastefully confectioned by Mr. Stokowski for his final effort. Amid the spoiled humanity of the "Symphonie Pathétique," the poussescafés of the "Nutcracker Suite," the subnormalities of the "1812 Overture," the young conductor sported. But even his sporting, like almost everything else he had been doing on the platform during the last two years, was wanting in abandon. The red lights burnt feebly. Never before had as little compulsion lain in his gestures. The orchestra remained tight and shut, reminded one at times of a violin of inferior make. The music of the self-pitiful Russ seemed thoroughly demoded, out-worn, obsolete, useless, and good only for the chamber of musical horrors. The audience, from its apathy, appeared to have gotten not a sensation. No trumpet-blast had set fire playing about the nipples. No parabola of the woodwind had serpentined up the spinal cord. Usually, the "Symphonie Pathétique" rouses "hurrahs," no matter how flatly it is presented, makes the clappers utter noises and high and extended "Yeas" at the conclusion of each movement. Usually, nothing conducted by the gentleman from Philadelphia, unless perchance it be a concerto in some one else's style by Emanuel Moor, fails to please an audience, ready as is his metropolitan to be delighted. But, on this evening, despite the warmth

139

of March, there was a notable coolness in and about Carnegie Hall. The audience resembled nothing so much as a child who, but a moment before the proud owner of a ruby air-sailing balloon, suddenly hears a slight report above him, and finds falling earthward a shriveled, dusky film. One was surprised that what had commenced as bravely as had the New York career of Mr. Stokowski should have developed a thing as empty as this concert. That was all.

Two years before, at the conclusion of the New York season of the Philadelphia Orchestra, the late James Huneker saw the young Polish-American conductor holding the metropolitan orchestral situation in his palm. Very few members of the concert-public did not at the time see eye to eye with the musicographer. Through the prevalent fog, the Stransky mist, the Damrosch mist, the Rabaud-Monteux mist, Mr. Stokowski had shone suddenly like the sun of ten o'clock. The concerts given in 1916 and 1917 for the Society of the Friends of Music, the five matinees given in 1918, had, it was perceived, introduced a veritably musical personage to the starved town. A man was throwing himself into the instrumental sea, making its waves vibrate and surge and foam with beauty, releasing himself through the tones cf the orchestra. The carpers who muttered "prima-donna conductor," and pointed disparagingly to the somewhat fatuous exhibition that was the performance of the Mahler "Symphonie der Tausend," were good-humoredly disregarded by a public impressed with the apparition.

For, if the man, in his years, was already as sensitive and elastic and sensuous as Mr. Stokowski showed himself to be, what might not be expected of him, so thoughts ran, as the passage of time matured and developed him, suppressed the self-consciousness and approfondized the feeling? One had, indeed, but to look at him, especially during the moments when he forgot himself and Aubrey Beardsley and moved unconstrainedly, to be assured of his latent mastery. The bodies of musicians, after all, quite as directly as their performance, reveal the nature of their gift. What externalizes itself in tone, is already evident previously in the coördination of the frame. You need not hear Mr. Walter Damrosch for instance in order to know what manner of conductor he is. You have but to observe him cross the platform, or to watch him using the muscles of his lower back in the effort to generate energy sufficient to permit him to swing out his arms, to have a complete mimetic equivalent for the quality of his musical performance. Nor was it necessary to hear Dr. Muck to know the fineness and sobriety of his direction. The man looked good-natured as an archfiend of Hell. But his great musicianship was in his gait and swing. And Mr. Stokowski, in his person, seemed to presage another epiphany of the good fire.

But it was only for a summer that the newcomer held, or seemed to be holding in the flat of his hand, the metropolitan situation. Immediately his winter began, it was evident that he was letting it dribble rapidly through his fingers. Neither that year, nor the succeeding, did Mr. Stokowski make anything notable of the immense opportunity offered him by his success. At the veritable beginning of his race, he appears to have thought it opportune to rest on his oars. One could not believe that he was earnestly working, delving, sweating. For he was not making great music live. The sensuous quality of his art, of course, had not abated. When the energy was in him, he could still entrance with some voluptuous piece of music, "Scheherazade," the "Tannhaüser" Bacchanale,

symphonies of the modern Frenchmen, there was never a
sign. Tchaikowsky, however, figured largely. The five
Orchestral Pieces of Schoenberg were promised among
the novelties, but nothing new save the "Italia" of Casella,
the poor stuff of Moor mentioned above, and the compositions of Cyril Scott, conducted by their author, was
played. There was a revival of "Tod und Verklärung" (a
veritable mania among conductors for being transfigured
and transfiguring others, exposed itself this season) and
a performance of the amorphous Requiem of Brahms.
But there was no grip in the season of Mr. Stokowski, no
enthusiasm, no faith, no redness and courage and energy.
The series of his concerts was yellow, tired, courageless.
At each performance, the conducting of the man seemed
to grow more vulgarly sensational. An afternoon concert
in January showed the old passion still there; showed
that it would relume at will. But it did not relume there-
after.

Still, one would not let go of him. One would not
resign oneself to expecting nothing of him. The man
was too musical a person not to compel one's faith even
when he was doing everything to dispel it. A blessing
was always about to come from him. And when it persisted in absenting itself, one was always ready to believe that it was just around the corner, and poised for
landing. It took some deed as raw, insolent, and impotent in conception, as impotent in execution as the all-
Tchaikowsky evening to disillusion one, and set the toy
balloon plunging earthward a wrinkled skin. At present,
we stand facing the coming seasons of the Philadelphia
Orchestra no less convinced than before of the latent
genius of the young conductor. We cannot forget the
moments when he makes his instrument sound sharp as
artillery and elemental as a whirlwind; and such, we

know, will probably from time to time come again. But, for the instant, we find ourselves in a very skeptical state of mind. We have caught sight of something a little vulgar in the man. The fine lyricism is mixed, now we know, with a something from which one wants to turn away. We have caught sight of a willingness to make a success on a low plane.

April, 1921.

The Group of Six

To the rattle of snare-drums and the crowing of toy-trumpets, a new band of youthful Parisians has paraded onto the musical boards. It is called the Group of Six; and there are five composers in it, one superfine, four fine. Durey was the sixth. But, being Ravelesque, an impressionist, and, it is not to be doubted, essentially respectable, he found himself out of place; and, a while since, resigned. There are five of them to-day; five fairly distinct persons who compose, nevertheless, a compact band. They hold ideas, views, theories, techniques, processes, exhibitions, and, probably, lady-loves in common. Their work stands distinct from other work, a thing by itself. Often, the work of one member resembles the work of another. But nothing quite like this music has ever before been made. Suppose a concert of new music, a concert without names, at which, among other modern things, some of the pieces of the Six were performed. You could not fail to recognize the group-men's for their own. You might not know which of them had done the thing. You might not like it. Or, you might like it for a while, and later find yourself a trifle strained and wearied. But you could scarce mistake it, not even for Strawinsky's, or Satie's, with which it has some relations. The group has authenticity.

The music of the men is full of edge; sharp, brusque, uncompromising. It comes at you like edges of paper,

146

rims of pressed rubber, blades of polished steel. There is no Debussyan fluidity, dreamfulness, satin. There is frowning mass; jagged, square outline. The polyphonies grind upon each other like millstones; grate and protest like metal parts borne heavily upon metal; like express-train wheels upon the rails down in bends of *subvia dolorosa*. The music starts suddenly and jerks, like machinery through which the brakes have been thrust. Sharpness and violence are in the acrid harmonies; the shrill and garish analine dyes of the instruments. The breath cuts into you, like ammonia.

Machinery is in the music of Strawinsky, too; and many moderns are working for severity of contour. But the Six-men's, on closer inspection shows a distinct individuality of substance. Their music is a startling mixture of archaism and hard bright modernity; of conservatism and the crassness of the streets and music-halls. The Six are oftentimes simply diatonic. Whole passages of their works do not budge from the safe c-major. They cling to it with an almost eighteenth-century fidelity; at times. Other times, they are to be found playing two diatonic figures in totally unrelated keys contrapuntally off against each other. One of their beloved tricks is to take a strong, rectilinear, even banal, melodic figure and envelop it and set it off in meshwork of acid, piercing polyphony. But, later, like prodigals, they return, and bask in the innocent sunshine of Mozart.

Tunes of all ages and sorts live in this element, like fish in the aquarium. Some have pastoral and eighteenth-century airs; strut like the rapid subjects of ancient symphonies; coquette like the flute tunes of antique duets. Others, might have figured in the defunct operas of Boieldieu and Adam; have a good-hearted stupidity.

But, by the side of these venerable figures, there come vulgar modern ones. Banal military marches trail their tatters through the orchestra. The music is full of effects and motives borrowed from jazz; wrenching and braying of brass. These men have had their ears opened to all forms of popular music of the day; jazz, ragtime, military signals, dance-tunes of negro and South-American orchestras, and even the canned and absurdly inhumanized expressions of gramophones, automatic pianos, orchestrelles, and stream-calliopes. In Milhaud's ballet, "L'homme et son désir," the brass roars forth brutal Brazilian dance-tunes. Sand-paper hisses, boards are beaten upon, whistles skyrocket and shrill. A rhythm of the drums imitates an exhaust. Human voices moan and sob as do those of nightmare-ridden sleepers. Milhaud has among his works a "shimmy," a "romance et rag-caprice." Auric, too, writes a brutal fox-trot "Adieu New York"; a joyous and ironic "Paris-Sport" which sounds as though his head were full of the timbres of *bals,* movies, cornet-music at national fêtes, carrousels, and pianolas.

This music makes its bow most unpretentiously. It seems gay, modest, discreet. Symphonies are not written for one hundred, two hundred, three hundred performers. Symphonies are not written for even sixty performers. Small bands of instrumentalists oftentimes suffice the group. Pastorales, suites, symphonies, serenades, are composed for ten, seven, sometimes even fewer players. Milhaud has a symphony for seven reeds. Brevity, also, is the soul of these men's wit. There is a general reaction from lengthiness everywhere. But none are so short as these young Parisians usually are. Their sonatas recall those of the early eighteenth century. Three brief vigorously contrasted movements can appease them:

"prelude, rustique, finale," say; each one requiring a few minutes in transit only. They seem to have learned from Strawinsky that music existed before the days of free fantasias and "developements."

It has, much of it, a sort of popular, easy, vulgar freedom, this music. Grandiloquence is not in it. Whatever flows from the stylographs of the group is as much at home in the vaudeville house and movie cavern as in the concert hall; could be played at fairs, on street-cars and ferry-boats. It seems to know the tricks and turns of the music-halls, the braying little bands; has seen the rectangles flicker on the silverscreen, and felt the abominable and gorgeous emotions awakened by the films. Like the music of Strawinsky, it takes us into gingerbread fairs, among carrousels, steam-calliopes, scenic railways, the imbecillic and glorious exhibitionism of the military parade, jazz bands in dance-halls, barmen mixing violent alcohols. Poulenc, for example, has little fanfares for fife and drum such as might appropriately be performed outside the walls of a side-show at a country fair; or by itinerant musicians at some crossroad; by soldiers loafing outside their barracks; before the rising of the curtian upon some acrobatics in a vaudeville. Into Auric's song, "Les joues en feu," again there has somehow gotten the boldness, the exaggeration, the crass coloring of the music-hall.

This music is at once charming and ill-mannered, gay and bitter, simple and scurrilous. There is much wit in it; many clever musical quotations—"Louise," Schubert's "Marche Militaire"; and not a little sarcasm. Auric writes joyously, ironically, a little scurrilously, as if fatigued by the incredible banality and idiocy of things. His lyricism is sweet as vitriol. "Je n'aime pas les catastrophes, les tragédies, les ruines," he says, "et je it often is, we respond with a sort of emotion. Only, we resent the output. For we see that what he excites in us is somehow old hat; the pawing over of old stuff. His own mind is not quite modern. It persists in dwelling amid objects whose reality has passed out of them. His "Roi David" puts us in touch with a state of a sort in which one holds conversations with God as with a kind parent, which is not at all to-day. Our religiosity expresses itself in more realistic forms. There is something derivative in all Honegger's moods. They come not so much from life as from other music. His pieces have some worth no doubt. He achieves the nude melodic line, the simplification, the absence of impressionist scintillance, to which the Six as a man aspire. But a work like his "Pastorale" for orchestra is almost painfully pastoral in character; reminiscent of a great many other men's landscape moods. His "Roi David" suggests very plainly the fact that the composer has been steeping himself in the work of the clavecinists antecedent to Bach. The passages of tender devotion, the little fugal battle pieces, sweet and simple as they are, recall a little too much another "David and Goliath"; that of Kuhnau. And so his music, stronger than Tailleferre's although it is, brings us something, too, which is never quite fresh.

III

With Poulenc, Auric, and Milhaud, we penetrate more closely into the heart of the artichoke. These are the men who indeed carry the group. Without them there would be no Six. What is really vital and daring in the work of the band flows from out of them. They have the bite, the courage, the brutality. They, too, are candidates more than musicians arrived. But each one has something new to give, and in all three one senses excellent possibilities.

Of the three, Poulenc is as yet the least developed. Auric is just as young in years as he; they were both of them born in 1899, later than the rest of the band; but Poulenc rests more juvenile. His music makes one represent him to oneself as a child playing gleefully with toys; chuckling and grinning and holding up objects to show them to the elders, and throwing them exuberantly about the nursery. He is gentle, amiable, and devoid of the cruel mockery which makes its appearance in Milhaud at times, and in Auric often. He comes out of "Petrushka"; but he has added Gallic salt and coolth to the playfulness of Strawinsky. He writes sophisticatedly childish tunes for the piano; rhythms repeated over and over again as the improvisations of children sometimes are; "perpetual movements," but subtly varied, subtly prevented from becoming monotonous. There is no one so simple or so complex, so young or so old, who would not smile with pleasure at hearing Poulenc's little gamineries. High spirits, wit, and animal grace break out of the merry brass in the "Overture" composed by him for Cocteau's "Spectacle-Concert." The best of his work is still contained in the setting of the *Bestiaire* of Guillaume Apollinaire for soprano, string quartet, flute, clarinet, and bassoon. We will not pretend that the work manifests a rich or a profound musical gift. The music is thin; and witty more than moving, although a genuine poetry sound from the last song, "Les Carpes." But it is exquisitely appropriate to the mood of Apollinaire's polished little epigrams; and lightly and surely executed. It is said that the newer of Poulenc's works exhibit a satisfactory development.

and vibrancy of his music is due his larger experience. His skill is very evident. He has learned to write for orchestra in such a manner that under his treatment small bands of instruments give forth volumes and sonorities which we commonly refer to the large size of the bands themselves. The music composed by him for "L'homme et son désir" has a most vigorous throat; and yet, the number of instruments demanded by the score, if we except the battery, which is fairly large, and the singing-voices, does not exceed fourteen. He has acquired a freedom with the percussion-pieces, which constitutes a little science. Like Satie and the rest of the Six, he has studied the noisemakers of the jazzbands for effects; and his orchestral works, the ballet and the ballade in particular, are hot and bright with color produced by tambourines, cymbals, bass-drums, triangle, celesta, sandpaper, clap-boards, whistles and other profane apparatus. His music, as a whole, is well written. With what elegance and quietude and humor has he not transcribed those jazzy tangos and Brazilian music-hall tunes! He has kept the melodic lines iron and clear among the dissonances; and still softened the banalities. The conflicts of rhythms, of tonalities, are managed with the utmost economy of emphasis. The elegant little vulgarisms cross races with real success; combine the artistry and delicacy of the French with the vigorous coarseness of the Spanish and Latin-American popular rhythms in most agreeable form.

Some principle older and less sharp of edge and more soaked with the sun than that of the other members of the Six must be in this composer, creating a terrain favorable to intellectual and acquired culture. Perhaps it is the rootfastness of generations; the century-long usedness to a certain condition of life, to certain series

of objects, which we in America have practically nothing
of, which liberates the man and harmonizes him. Suavity
and voluptuousness and liqueur-like richness must be in
the plasm itself. Hence, even within the limits of the
intellectualized group-expression; even among externally
grasped and not quite approfondized ideas, Milhaud
achieves a density and a weight which distinguishes the
body of his work. Auric, and Poulenc in a lesser degree,
may both of them be truer to themselves and more fundamentally expressive within the limits of the common
mannerisms of the group, impudence, violence, irony.
Milhaud's hand remains the happier, more delicate and
gratifying. It may even be that the refinement present
in his personality is lodged there as something of an
unwelcome guest; as something which the possessor
would gladly exchange for the hardness, the lighter and
tougher entrails of his two fellows. Nevertheless, the
density and brownness of blood stands this one in good
stead, and signals him, despite his defects as the artist.

Variety of mood further sets the work of Milhaud
apart from that of the others. To be sure, he remains
the faithful partisan in whatever form he attempts. The
common baggage of the movement, diatonic passages,
little cocky-doodle-doo's for orchestra, excruciatingly dissonant contrapuntal effects, jazz-rasps and jerks, strut-
ting march-rhythms, are carried through the range of his
compositions. The hardness of edge, legacy of Berlioz,
affected by him; the mordant irony; the broad grin with
which much of the stuff is presented, are not his alone.
But the Latin-American dance-hall tunes which he utilizes
extensively are his own *trouvaille*. He appears to have
become familiar with them during his sojourn as attaché
in Brazil and to have conceived the hope of doing with
them what Chabrier and Bizet did with their Spanish

forbears. And the range of forms to which he has set
hand, is unusually wide. He has written for piano, for
voice and piano, for violin and piano, for oboe, clarinet,
flute and piano, for large and chamber orchestras. The
music composed by him for the theatre includes a strictly
operatic setting of the "Eumenides" of Æschylus; incidental music for the "Choephores" and the satyr-play of
Claudel, ballet-music and the accompaniment to a pan-
tomine-farce. He has made songs on fragments of the
tender and anguished letters of Eugénie de Guérin and
on the sneering little "Soirées de Pétrograd" of René
Chalupt. The list of his compositions includes sonatas
and sonatines, symphonies, and serenades classical in
intention; a neurasthenic "Psalm" for men's chorus; and
a "shimmy" for jazz-band, a tango for the clowns of the
Cirque Médrano, a "romance and rag-caprice" and a col-
lection of Brazilian dances. And, to a certain extent, he
has entered all these different subjects. The exuberant,
obstreperous incidental music for "Protée" has Gallic
gayety and verve and salt. There is something of real
hysterical overwroughtness in "L'homme et son désir"
and in the song "La limousine." And the ballade for
orchestra, and "Le Boeuf sur le Toit" and the "Suadades
do Brazil" show genuine feeling for the full-blooded
character of the popular musical expressions of the day.

But although the ground-plan of Milhaud's work is
vaster than Poulenc and Auric's, the building seems
somewhat shaky. His compositions exhibit musicianly
tact of a superior sort, and marvelously alert sensibili-
ties; they also exhibit power in a state of dissipation. It
is seldom one of them thoroughly compels the interest
on second hearing. What they have in them of reality,
the smell of the crowd, the millstone-like grinding of
steely polyphonies, the iron contours, nervous sudden

unprepared contrasts of louds and softs, bright color and brisk movement, freedom from romantic exaltation and the jewelry of the impressionists, evaporates too quickly. The garish hue of the instruments has too little body. The pungency and high spirits grow thin. On first acquaintance, "L'homme et son désir" was poisonous and terrible. The human voices crying as they cry out of nightmares; the savage banging of the percussion; whistles and wan monotonous flutes and brutal blaring of the horns, seemed to be carrying the enervation of fierce tropical nights, the states of utter dejection when the whole force of nature seems bent on dissolving the character in slime, and no doorway offers escape, the mad dance of inhuman rejected instincts, the depleted morning hours. One felt the music miasmal and suffocating as dead August nights and stagnant-green; the instrumentation the very edge of to-day. But on second acquaintance, the baleful potency was out of it. The score was wearing sheer. It seemed the scratching of a surface, not the penetration of the subject-matter. The nerves only had been touched. The music wanted suspense and cumulative effect. A third hearing intensified the impression given by the second. The flute-gurgling music which accompanied the gyrations of the two women about the helplessly winding man; and the music of final exhaustion seemed a trifle insipid. Indeed, the interpolated Brazilian tunes set in the score began to appear the most vital substance in the work.

v

The weaknesses of Milhaud's music; the weaknesses of the work of the entire Six; lie in the unclarity of the motive which drives them all.

The impulse in them begins as a vital, necessary movement. Somewhere in the Six, there is the push that is evolving the art of music. Behind them, one feels Moussorgsky sitting and writing his unpretentious, popular, miraculous little things; humorous, ironic, stripped of everything not to his purpose. Behind them, there is the gay scandal of Strawinsky; the free, Dionysiac polyrhythms of "Petrushka" and the "Sacre," unrhetoric polyharmonics, the taste of cool, crude earth; and Satie, uneager to be the savior of the universe, putting down his modest, delicate designs for his own pleasure. They, too, these young Frenchmen, are carried forward by the movement in life which is seeking to make man discard the sense of his importance, his centrality in the scheme of the universe, and is actually tending to make him more self-reliant and human. Absolute truths, immutable systems, fixed concepts, c-major scales, equal temperament, they are no longer in the center of the arena. What has come to stand there is the need of rendering as exact an image of the thing which exists; the need, irrespective of tradition, irrespective of what the past has handed down, of approximating the machinery of music, the tones of instruments, to what is quivering and sounding and starting in men this very day. And to this need, the Six commence a response.

They, too, in answer to the modern sense, are moving to recapture the balance which the eighteenth century began to have and the nineteenth came near losing; the capacity of seeing in everything, great and little, one thing; of being light without being trivial; of not forgetting amid the tragic and solemn aspects of life, the sly winking joke of it all. It was with this balance, this sense of the universal, in minuet or catastrophe, game of blind man's buff or symphony, that Mozart and

Haydn brushed their tears away, and remained the sovereign, sane, and healthful minds. Beethoven and Wagner had it far less. In them began a kind of heaviness, a gesture of grandeur, which threatened at moments to become pompousness; and did end in the Titanism of Mahler and Strauss. What one heard was—sixteen horns. With Moussorgsky, a reaction commenced. He had a way of writing for the orchestra and the entire operatic machine so that folksongs, little dances, childish scenes, jokes, even, fitted perfectly into the atmosphere of tragedy and suffering. He had a sense of life fresher and directer than any of his contemporaries; a closeness to the realities that comes like the cold good air.

The understanding of the beauty of the modern freshness of will is in the Six, also. They hear in Bizet's direct speech what Nietzsche heard there, too, the free acceptance of one's fate, the resolution to perform the thing which one has to do; and hold it high like him, above the division in the will of Wagner and Brahms and the other cultured north-Europeans. That is what repells the Six from Debussy, with his irresolution, his tendency to evasion, his preference of the solitary dream. They feel the necessity of making a music more grim, more on the earth, more sharp and sudden in its decisions; a music fuller of the hardness and athleticism and robustezza of men who choose, who dare to cut and act and go, who face the grim reality of human life and nevertheless accept it and live themselves through. Like Bloch, like Bartók, like Strawinsky, they are almost unconsciously being impelled to move toward the solidity, the violence and maleness which Cézanne added onto impressionism; and which music, still too impressionistic in quality, requires lest it lose its power.

What is watery, savorless, stale, in the Six comes from

an untruthfulness to this modern movement, a deflection of its natural course. The Six have by no means generally the courage of themselves and to themselves; if they think they have, then their right hand is unaware of what their left hand is doing. Satie has said of Ravel that while his mouth rejects the ribbon of the legion of honor, his music demands it. Far truer is it that the Six, while outwardly rejecting the attitude of self-importance, the look of responsibility, dignity, and grandeur, inwardly persist in the sort of self-conceit which their lips deny. We have already seen a good old-fashioned feeling of the omnipotence of his thoughts revealed by Honegger in the God-conversations of his "Roi David." The old infantile egoism persists in the others, too, in other forms. It is very patent in Milhaud. He affects the self-forgetfulness, the humility and warm human feeling of the eighteenth century men. But he does not really understand it. He is attracted by it; but, instead of taking courage from it, and going his own way, he falls to imitating its outward forms. He, too, has erected P. E. Bach and Mozart and Mendelssohn into a sort of absolute truth. We find him hiding in the shadow of the rock of his absolute; proclaiming a sort of apostolic succession and laying-on of hands in music; asserting that he and his band are the sole conservors of the classic proportions of Mozart and Mendelssohn amid the machinery and jazz of the advancing century. He will have it that his serenade has the proportions of those of Mozart; we find him using Mozartean tunes and Mozartean rhythms. But, as in all cases in which reverence for the past cloaks mere desire for disinfection and sanctification, the traditionalism of Milhaud has resulted only in dead children. His classical stretches are without form, empty and sterile. For his own spirit, and,

therefore, the spirit of the classic masters, has remained
shut to him.

In running from self-determination, the Six run from
their subject-matter, too. Their gesture says "Look, we
dare do the light, the little things, like Rameau, like
Mozart! We dare be popular, be playful, like Bizet and
Chabrier! We are not saving the world!" But the urbanity, the lightness of touch, reveals itself oftentimes a
sort of slap-dash impotence, an impudent disregard of the
subject-matter, of the dignity of the craft, and of the
rights of the public. They begin with the modern feeling,
the desire to acquit themselves of as exact a representation of the existent matter as they can achieve with their
technique. But the most of them, Milhaud, for instance,
cannot completely carry through; cannot lose themselves
in their subjects; cannot make the thing round and vital
in itself. Milhaud's work seems at times a perpetual
glancing-off from states of incandescence. He cannot
give himself completely to any work. The glare and labor
and self-obliteration of creation seem to affright him. He
is finished too quickly with each of his compositions;
over-ready to chase off and attack a new subject before
he has really mastered the old; over-eager to have his
work printed and out in the world proclaiming his name.
It is as something of a Don Juan among the music-staves
that he appears to us. The fish is not more prolific than
he; but of the eggs he scatters upon the flood few hatch
completely free-swimming organisms. The person who
declared that each composition of Milhaud contains at
least one interesting idea spoke an almost final word.

In the relation of the Six to the popular expressions of
the day, there is visible the result of a third great deflection of impulse. They have misunderstood the promptings
in them beaconing toward a great decisiveness, ruthless-

ness, directness of musical attack. They feel its beauty in Bizet and Chabrier. They thrill when Nietzsche demands of music "the salt and fire and the great compelling logic, the light feet of the south, the dance of stars, the quivering dayshine of the Mediterranean." But once again, they run away from the act they have to perform. What the German wanted of musicians was the sign, the breath, the reality of the state in man that loves its fate; that does not evade the necessary choice; that measures itself always against the impossible thing, lives dangerously, makes the selection of the higher, further, more perilous, more exacting; leaps out of itself and beyond itself. And what the Six have done, is to make heroes of Bizet and Chabrier, just as they have made heroes of Mozart and P. E. Bach; and, at the same time, to run away from the doorway through which their heroes started to go. Instead of becoming choice-men, they have nourished a perverse desire to revert to the type of men who have no serious choices to make. Instead of dreaming of becoming aristocrats of the spirit, they have dreamt of becoming like to the common man, whose acts come easy because they are half reflex; whose responses no preconception, no inner elegance and refinement limits and conditions a priori; for whom no individual woman but only the sex exists. Hence, the peculiar fascination exercised on them by the musical expressions of the proletariat and of America, in which the choicelessness lives; jazz, ragtime, mechanical music of all sorts; and their curious fashion of handling it. For their adapted motives are not really synthecized and essentialicized by them. These men are not Strawinskys and Sandburgs. What they find they scarcely alter. Their jazzing, their fox-trots, shimmies, rag-caprices, are imitative, largely. And for all its surface brightness, this music bores us almost as quickly as the jazz without the wrong notes.

Small wonder, though, that the Six are none of them really more than half and half; none of them as yet fully foaled and free! They are young men; and the current of life bears against them. Their France, too, is trying to dodge the necessity of having to go through a certain door. She, too, is seeking not to make the choice she has to make, the choice of the new European coöperation, perilous, higher, further; and trying to revert to the habits of times gone by, to the manners of celebrated thugs, Richelieu, the Sun King, Napoleon; trying to avoid throwing her Heart of Wallace into the welter and finding it there again in triumph.

They will have to learn to stand alone, to fare alone, these group-men. They will have to find chart and compass within themselves; forget Cocteau and his estheticism and the man who named them Group of Six; forget the proportions of Mozart and the Latin Genius and what other musicians are doing. The artist is ever a man who walks alone. Self-sufficiency, self-determination, carelessness of what men say or do or understand, trust in what is pushing and urging and speaking deep within him, all the anti-social virtues; they are what give him his value. The more he is the tramp, unrespectable, resident of a world proper to himself, the more he serves. To-day, the Group of Six may still have the reality it had a few years since. It came out of a common experience in a number of individuals. It was formed probably for purposes of self-protection in the hostile environment which is outside and inside the men of every new generation. There had to be a wedge for the attack on the fortress of the established ideas. To-morrow, it may be, the reality will with-

draw itself from the group. The men are known, respected, granted a hearing. In persisting, it may defeat
its own purpose. They are a danger, groups. They make
it far too easy for the members to avoid becoming their
own justificators; substitute the law of the herd, always
inferior, for the law of the individual. The tendency to
evade is already too strong in the Six. Only by showing
itself an instrumentality whereby some young ones have
gotten themselves the rich courage to their own thoughts,
will the Group of 1919 prove itself of worth, and create
its own past. And that proof can be given only by men
who leave their fathers' houses indeed, leave all the caves
and shelters of the tribe, and go their own and solitary
ways.

September, 1921.

John Alden Carpenter

OUT in Chicago, underneath a green and white marquee, there sits a composer. Our thoughts wander his way not unoften. Especially when we see, all over Europe, the black bole of the musical tree shrill again with infant green: Group of Six tum-ti-tumming it joyously upon the banks of the Seine; young school in Poland, very delicate, very elegant, and not too wishy-warshau; Spanish music kicking out alive and tough and stiff underneath De Falla's hand; disciples about Schoenberg opening dark sayings upon the harp; especially then, when we hear all these new musics from oversea, does our thought strike suddenly in the direction of John Alden Carpenter's.

A reaction of the sort is fairly normal to the minds of the greater number of the younger American workers. They are self-conscious; and impulses received from outre-mer readily convert themselves in their breasts into movements of self-analysis. The members of the newer generations do not go long without once or twice furtively casting the eye over the national condition. It is in them, they know; and they are part of the three-thousand-mile-spreading thing. Every throb of life which debauched old Europe even in her stews manages to communicate, impels them to attack again, and worry the hoary problem of native incapacities. It is not at all uncommon for young Americans in Paris who come from assisting at the performance of a Cocteau ballet or at a concert of the work of the Group of Six, to go sit at a café-table half the night, discussing over the bocks the question why, not Chartres and the Sainte-Chapelle, but things as irresponsible and spontaneous and to-dayish as these Gallic entertainments, cannot be produced t'other side the Atlantic. Evening after evening, over the heads of a bunch of such, arguing and soliloquizing as though they were Russians out of Turgenev, there quivers like a humming-bird stationary on air, mute, rigid, ecstatic, a tiny wingèd Van Wyck Brooks, and one perceives the sparkling of his keen gray eyes, his grin like a pleased savage's, hears the agitation of his wings. Wherever two or three of the musical persuasion are met together, whether in Europe or over here at home, like as not they will strike along the path cut by him, and fall a-wondering why life doesn't turn itself into music in the New World, where water contains as much of the elixir of art as it does in the Old, and where men stalk about on their hind legs, too. There are instruments here, and people to play upon them, and others who will go hear performances. There is the art of Europe to serve as tradition. We'd like much to find a composer here who'd furnish us with solid mattter into which we could bite with all the jaw. We need composers; men to express themselves and us in music; it's no longer a matter of decoration.

And then, your pondering music-lovers will turn in a sort of frenzy, and search the native field once more. "I will not let thee go unless thou bless me." It must be some one real has been overlooked. It must be an injustice has been done to an American composer merely because he is an American. Jamesesque sentiment of herd-inferiority has caused men to see Europe and her music-makers through stained-glass spectacles. Why should not an American composer be as able as a Frenchman or Pole or Viennese to seize upon the elements of existence and transmute them to music? There must be, on these shores, at this very moment, two or three native-born musicians of creative audition. It is then, however, that the mind finds the man of the striped awnings in Chicago; and dissuaded from further inquisitiveness, stands stunned.

Of the workers at play in the field of American music, none, we are assured, were self-realization a possibility for the native-born composer, would stand more directly in the way of success than John Alden Carpenter. It is for that reason our thought goes direct to him. Other personalities in the field are, it may be, inherently finer, warmer, more thoroughly sympathetic. There are several one respects more both as human beings and as potential fountains of music. But the Chicagoan's resources are coördinated to a degree approximated by no other young American composer. Neither Engel, Powell, Morris, nor any of our other hopefuls have themselves as well in hand as has he. Without denying for an instant that a course in composition under some great magister would help him from the root up, one can still aver that among all the fœtuses in the arcana, he is the nearest birth. And at forty-five years of age even an American artist is moulded. At moments, particularly in the second movement of the concertino, with its five-eight beat, its extended swing, its traveling salesman sort of life, Carpenter's music crosses the line that separates the unborn from the born and is clothed in the colors of existence. The man has even attained a certain liberation of fantasy. He toys engagingly with his orchestra. Something of the humor of the jazz-band got into his "Krazy Kat" score; the opening snore is in the grand style. The piano is remarkably well treated as an instrument of percussion in the Concertino. Indeed, the work exhibits a keen sensibility to the qualities of the various pieces of the battery;

kettle drums, bass drum, cymbals, tambourine, castanets and glockenspiel—demonstrates the sensitivity of the composer's epidermis. Aquatints wash charmingly across the orchestra of the "Perambulator" suite; the scene of the mock bullfight in "The Birthday of the Infanta" is brilliant with its trumpet passages.

But with these gifts Carpenter has succeeded in producing chiefly some comfortable music. His forms are not so much the very objects of emotion as means of suggesting emotion about something not stated. The *lento grazioso* of the Concertino is, after all, a very exceptional passage in a body of a work that scarcely ever permits one to experience. The suite, "In a Perambulator," for example, is not so much the world of the child felt directly as it is the adult comment on the sensations of the baby carriage. You have but to compare it with "The Children's Corner" of Debussy and "Ma Mère l'Oye" of Ravel to perceive its pseudo-realism. The two Frenchmen managed to coincide intuitively with the child. The American, with all his charming talent for light orchestration, his wit and musical good manners, causes us more to smile at a world made miniature and playfully ironic than feel the terror, the buzz and glow of the universe of the nursery. There is no poetry in the work. It moves us not. "Krazy Kat," also, falls between stools; it does not take jazz and transform it into rhythm. Nor does Carpenter's ballet, "The Birthday of the Infanta," after the fairy story of Oscar Wilde, express the limbus infantiorum in which the composer and so many of his co-workers find themselves, and put us in touch with a reality. It was indubitably the portal out of his own world of fantasy which the action of the ballet opened to him, that drew the composer to the subject. For to have realized indeed a musical atmosphere for the scene of the dim Escorial, the monstrous etiquette hedging about the royal child, the immense hoopskirts on the slim young body, the toy bull-fight, the grotesque capers of the impassioned dwarf, the entire strange little subterranean world, would have been, in a fashion, to objectify himself. But, even here, Carpenter showed how almost impossible it is for him to perform an act of imagination. The music is not the expression of the composer's sensations and ideas. It does not pierce out from some hidden center. One feels it has been "made" rather self-consciously. This is music as decoration. On the whole, it is pleasant enough, but not exciting to the mind. One rather likes the dreamy dances of the first scene and the burlesque *tauro-machia*. One rather dislikes the close of that scene, where the dwarf decides to make his way into the palace, the interlude, and all the rest of the business where Carpenter seeks to be dramatic and passionate. For there, he is helpless. One feels the wish; but the performance is both hectic and banal. He seems incapable of facing the situation, of making it with his own blood; and we are not surprised to find him fumbling with vaguely Debussy-like material. It seems unfortunately as though the way lay entirely clear for the qualification of Franz Schreker as the composer of the only "Birthday of the Infanta." John Alden Carpenter, after all, remains a musical embryo, man-sized, but nevertheless an embryo.

Carpenter is nearly as clever with words as he is with the orchestra; the little homage to Herriman prefixed to the score of "Krazy Kat" is a nice piece of real wit; and we are therefore not surprised to find that he has written words which accuse him no less than does his music. When the "Concertino" was produced in its original form in Chicago in 1916, he wrote:

The "Concertino" is, in effect, a light-hearted conversation between piano and orchestra—as between two friends who have traveled different paths and become a little garrulous over their separate experiences. The rules of polite talk, as always, between friends, are not strictly observed—often, in animated moments, they talk both at once, each hearing only what he says himself. Presently the moment comes, as always, between friends, when no conversation is necessary—a relaxed moment, when Friendship itself takes them in hand, and they have nothing to say.

Is that not the tone by which Carpenter can be known among the musicians? Bach, one knows, loved music as though it were the angel of deliverance and death. Beethoven loved it as though it were the spirit of liberty, present, like Leonore in that of Florestan, in the dungeon of mankind. And Chopin loved music as though it were a luxurious mistress riding him to death; and Schumann worshiped it with a sort of sweet calf-love all his life, long after he had gotten beyond the age of seventeen; and Brahms, as though it were a woman whom he might never possess, for all his great adoration, because she was the wife of another. But, with John Alden Carpenter, we are no longer in the region where men go heavy with the load of the beauty and awfulness of human life. We have left the great swelling hills and apocalyptical skies of passion. We have reached eminently safe ground. The rules of politeness are not strictly observed, and "there is still so much that presses to be said on a pleasant night— between friends."

So, on that day, we read no longer in the book; we fare no further than the green and white marquee. The case throws into light something we know within us, knew all the while foreign enterprise made us revolt against it, made us hope to prove it untrue. We see again the sickly tenderness in the American breast; in all of us; in men who are as agile as this Chicagoan, in men who will never attain even the facility he has developed. Why it is that sustained feeling is a thing too unbearably painful for us, we cannot say. The feat of letting the thing happen to him; of letting the fierce glare beat on his exposed flesh, and of responding to it by registering severe inbiting line upon line, can be easy for no man anywhere, whether in Europe or this side the sea. And still, the old world seems never to be without some few men who are exposing the naked breast. Many men, poets, musicians, painters, are facing the glow. But here, in the new, such men do not come; no more than one or two are working. Here, the light glares in upon us like a Medusa head. The light is the burning woman-face that turns to stone. It is as though the breasts in all of us were sore, sore from birth, and unable to bear the embrace of life; and shrank away into sick roselands; chocolate and newspapers; speech and vague remarks and movies. And there we play, madman-like, with children's toys. Like Carpenter, we write sentimental war songs to hymn tunes. Like Davies, cuddle ourselves in fantasies. When we criticize, we urge upon the country the moral resolutions that produce art. And heaped about us, fresh-tumbled out by nature at every moment, there lies the gorgeous stuff we cannot use.

September, 1921.

Satie and Impressionism

"Socrate" has made grave the figure of Erik Satie. The tiny symphonic drama, based on fragments of the "Symposium," the "Phædrus," and the "Phædo," has given it something of the dignity of those of the composers who have felt life simply and generously. Before the nude, unpretentious little score was published, one conceived the good man first the clown of music. The tragedian one saw in him second always. Debussy, Rimsky, Strauss, Ravel; all the musicians of the time who were intrigued by the mysterious presence of the other senses, sight, smell, touch, as overtones in the sense of hearing, and who dreamt of stirring all five senses at once, of composing perfumes, lights, textures—these appeared the serious performers. Satie, like the sly zanies of the circus, waltzed in at the conclusion of the acrobatics to burlesque them. All hampering, impeding magnificence and ineffectual beauty and color misplaced; he came to humiliate the excessive pride and complacency of the exhibitors by reminding the audience and them of the complete indifference of the universe to such human accomplishments and prowesses. He, too, in the region of music, lost his brilliant trousers while parading, and stumbled over his own feet just as he had succeeded in getting all six oranges revolving in air.

Indeed, so delicious and biting was the clown-play that it is possible Satie has already, or will shortly, put a close for the present to impressionistic music-making. The partisans of absolute music found in him a champion, perhaps not of the sort they preferred, but one very service-able, nevertheless. The bladder he wielded struck double blows always, one to the theory of program-music, the other to the practice of its votaries. The first he made ridiculous by forcing it to logically illogical extremes. There can be no doubt, of course, of the fact that tones, phrases, timbres, excite visual images in composer and auditor. And still, it is equally sure that the images evoked are by no means inevitably identical. The ver-dict of the lady who held that Beethoven's piano sonata opus 27 No. 2 is called the "Moonlight" for the reason that the second movement resembles so much the shine of the moon on Lake Lucerne, amply instances the rule. Music is too idealistic a thing to permit itself to be bound to concrete references. You cannot have a white horse in music. It was precisely the white horse that Satie mischievously pretended to make his music represent. In a series of burlesque "program" compositions for piano, "Descriptions automatiques," "Embryons desséchés," "Croquis et agaceries d'un gros bonhomme en bois," and others, he joined some sophisticatedly banal and childishly absurd music to very detailed and concrete arguments. Several of these parodies, "Sur un vaisseau," "Tyrolienne turque," "Españaña," pretend to atmospheres much in fa-vor with Debussy, Ravel, and Albeniz. In each, the pro-gram is made ludicrous through the perfect meaningless-ness of the music. One is reminded continuously of the powerlessness of music to be concretely narrative and pictorial. The idiotic figures of "Embryons desséchés" are supposed to describe minutely the habits of sea-slugs and other crustaceans. A sort of hunting theme of the kind that is given hapless infants to play in the first year of their pianism is supposed to describe the manner in which the Podophthalmia pursues its prey. The mock-nautical figures of "Sur un vaisseau" have attached to them words that inform the performer that the music is to represent, among other things, a breath of wind, maritime melancholy, the captain's remark, "Très beau voyage," a distant landscape, waves, and the landing stage. The allegedly "Spanish" music of "Españaña" illustrates "La belle Carmen et le peluquero," the Puerta Maillot, the good Rodriguez, the remark, "Isn't that the Alcade?" the Plaza Clichy, and the rue de Madrid.

Besides these particular slaps at the theory of program music, Satie, in all his pieces, mocks the descriptive, definitive music with burlesque and impossible directions to the performer. Even in his delicate lissome dances, "Gnossiennes," "Gymnopédies," as he entitles them, one reads continually suggestions such as "Arm yourself with clairvoyance," "Counsel yourself meticulously," "Carry this sound further off," and "Open the head." Otherwheres, one reads "In the manner of a nightingale with a toothache," "Epotus, Corpulentus, Caeremoniosus, Paedogogus," "From the end of the eyes and withheld in advance," "A little bloodily," "Without blushing a finger," "On yellow plush," "Dry as a cuckoo." The "Prélude de la porte héroïque du ciel," that wicked, amusing parody on the prelude to "The Blessed Damozel" by Debussy, is interlined with directions to the performer to play, "superstitiously, with deference, very sincerely silent, without pride, and obligingly." One is reminded a little of some of Percy Grainger's directions. The chief difference between the two types, however, is that these of the Frenchmen are funny without being vulgar.

But if Satie hit the theory of program music smartly in his "tone-poems" he buffeted the impressionistic musicians themselves even more stingingly. For if his parodies adumbrate the cardinal disability of music, they de-

clare very plainly the fact that the program had helped
those who used it to make things fairly easy for themselves. The suggestions of titles and arguments had made
it a simple matter to obtain effects with music without
really making the music do all the work. Strauss, for
example, had come to rely more and more upon elaborate
programs to give point to a good deal of uninteresting
music, and make foolish titterings of the violin appear to
say something profound about the capriciousness of
women. Debussy, too, had suggested by means of his
jeweled and precious titles moods which the music either
did not need or did not justify. And as we play over the
music of "Españaña" and "Sur un vaisseau," and contrast
it with the mock-local color of the interpolations, Puerta
Maillot, Plaza Clichy, it comes to us that we have been
lending our imaginations a little too cheaply to the impressionists. At the command of titles and programs, we
have set an elaborate stage in our minds for the musician;
seen some sort of literesque Spain when he has spoken
"La soirée dans Granade" or "Ibéria" or "Rapsodie Espagnole"; some sort of romantic sea when the word was
"Un barque sur l'océan" or "La mer"; and been ready to
lend out our imaginations cheaply. No matter what the
intrinsic value of the music of Debussy and Ravel and Al-
béniz is, and we do not for a moment wish to belittle its
loveliness, it still seems to us that the attribution of romantic titles to compositions is an unfairness committed
to the auditor. A sort of violence is done his imagination.
One should be permitted to hear music as music, and create one's own images, if images one must create. Titles
like those which Debussy strewed about so freely constitute a sort of assault; even when they do not assist the
composer to gain illegitimate effects with his work. And
one turns with relief to the humorous, modest, unpretend-

ing names, "Trois morceaux en forme de poire," "Airs à faire fuir," "Véritables préludes flasques," "Danses de travers," which Satie has given to some of his most diaphanous compositions. These little jokes, at least, make no pretense. They leave one be in one's voyage through the musical pages marked by them. And the voyage often leads one to the very soul of music.

For Satie, like his brethren of the circus, is a good acrobat. The clowning and parody of the zanies oftentimes conceal an art as delicate as that of the legitimate performers. And if Satie's talent is not a very rich or very powerful one, it is nevertheless exquisite and original and real. Even in his broadest pieces of fun, his horsiest horsing of Debussy and Ravel, a real musical wit points the satire. Debussy's complacent *tristezza,* his softly wailing arpeggios and consecutive minor triads, are very slyly taken off, reduced with no little artfulness to a comic banality; and though the song on the words beginning *Dis-moi, Daphénéo, quel est donc cet arbre dont les fruits sont des oiseaux qui pleurent?* burlesques the lachrymosity, yearnfulness, and pleasure-painfulness of Ravel's lyrics, a very limpid and gossamer-like music accompanies the fun. And Satie's less ironic work, his delicate, curiously simple, whole-tone-scale pieces for piano, are both poetic and interesting in form. Never, perhaps, has an atom of the living Apollo been incarnated in more unprepossessing matter. The gift of Satie, the power of momentary genial play with tone, is a bit of purity thrown into a heap of rubble. Neither variety nor extended form are latent in it. It is a vein of sudden visitations only, sudden genial movements of music with the capacity for pricking and exciting the ear with novelties of line and rhythm; and it does not trickle often. Were Satie not as cute as he is; were he without his healthy humility, his good-nature

perspective on himself, it might easily have been abused,
spoilt in the forcing-process to which so many a slight
and real talent has been subjected by an unwise possessor.
The man has the capacity for producing trash; an occasional pot-boiler demonstrates the fact only too plainly;
and, were his balance a little less sure, he might have
spent his life adding terrible grand opera upon terrible
grand opera to the number of terrible grand operas
already in existence. Fortunately, he has not needed to
see himself writing "great" music. He has been able to
listen for his diminutive vein; to let it murmur its few
measures when it will; and then to set them down for
what they may be worth.

His output is not large, although want of facilities for
publication has probably made it seem smaller than it is
indeed. Now that the charm of his music is being recognized, it can be seen that he has been steadily working on
his little things through the years. What he has written
for the piano has the charm of objects born in a medium.
As one traces the gentle arabesques of his "moments
musicaux" over the keys, one hears again the piano. One
is really, once again, "playing the piano" for the sake of
the play. His little suite, "Trois morceaux en forme de
poire," even makes four-hand music a delight both for
auditor and performer, so pianistically and subtly are
the movements written. It is particularly in his excessively simple and yet wavering gliding melodic lines that
he has been most successful. Less fecund in harmonic
and coloristic invention than some of his contemporaries,
Satie has nevertheless created for himself a personal idiom
through his inventions in melodic form. It is his theory
that we have reached an end of harmonic invention; and
that the avenue of development open to music leads
through "form," through the process of contrasting and

playing against each other rhythms and masses. And, in practice, we find him achieving curious, intriguing balances and pricking melodic patterns, by contrasting and opposing to each other set periods, and phrases of unequal lengths and different characters. An irregular form is established; we are always catching our breaths in surprise at the unsuspected turnings which his music takes. There is a sort of charm in the nocturnes, the pieces in which this curious sense of form has been most successfully produced; a charm which one does not seem able quite to surmount and rationalize. Nor is one ever irritated, as one sometimes is by a fellow-adventurer of Satie's, Milhaud, by the breath of an arbitrary will, a purely perverse desire to be surprising and disconcerting in his melodic line. Satie remains the musician. He has always had the rare gift of being utterly simple, tender and direct. The second of the three "Véritables préludes flasques" catches the attentiveness and sadness of the waiting dog with delicious sureness, and with an utter simplicity of means. The little piece is no more than a two-voice invention. One must go to Chopin's mazurkas to find piano music as nude in line, as simple in means and yet as graceful and charming and satisfying as Satie's nocturnes, his "Morceaux" and "Gnossiennes." A sort of white and agreeably monotonous beauty pulses through these utterly unpretentious things, and calls to mind the impersonality and slowness and sleepiness of certain oriental dancers. Only, there one sees in the mind, if a momentary relapse be permitted one, a severe Greek temple-yard, and the athletic limbs of Dorian maidens.

That one perceived first, however, the more destructive side of Satie's criticism of musical impressionism, the clowning; and second, always the more constructive, is due chiefly to the fact that although the good man's talent was always a very real and exquisite one, it is recently only, roundly since Satie's fiftieth birthday, that it has attained maturity. It was within very sharply defined limits that he was able to work. Although he was younger than Debussy by very few years, and although he taught the Parisian magician much, the use of consecutive ninths, the use of certain church modes, and other refinements; he was always most successful in the smaller forms. His invention was far too thin to permit him to essay the long curve, the complicated pattern. There are even pure and limpid sketches of his that make us merely to feel that the composer deserves the name of artist chiefly because he knows when to stop; another few bars, and we might commence to grow a little weary.

It may be that a course of study undertaken at the Schola Cantorum during the year 1911 helped Satie in his development; although the immediate result, a prelude, chorale and fugue entitled "Aperçues Désagréables" does not suggest that its author found much to delight him in the post-Franckian discipline. What probably proved itself more decisive was the sympathy which came to him, during the years of the war, from some of the younger musicians and critics. In Jean Cocteau, Satie found both a prophet and a stimulating collaborator. With him he composed the ballet "Parade." The members of the Group of Six brought him esthetic corroboration. A few intelligent amateurs commenced to recognize the genuineness of his gift; and the Princess Edmond de Polignac ordered "Socrate" of him. In the two works produced under the direct stimulation of his friends, Satie has given himself at his largest. Both works very decisively reveal his particular orientation to musical art. The ballet shows him very deliberately rejecting all grandiosity of material; all grandiloquence of style; holding to a nude, unemphatic elegance. He is content to take the material, the tone of his work, from off the streets. The imitation of the sounds of revolvers and typewriting machines in the orchestra is symbolic of a general effort to capture something characteristic in color, in timbre, of the ordinariness of life; to play the circus, too. *La petite fille Americaine* dances to a sort of essentialized ragtime. The Chinaman's little fugato has the unpretentious quality, the slightly down-at-the-heel animality of the vaudeville turn. And the music is innocent of scene-painting, of illustration in the impressionistic sense. It is straight design: delicate, frivolous, sophisticated; "un peu de musique" which dances its way as self-consistent as a movement of a Haydn quartet, and breaks off and ends without ceremony.

Perhaps even more definitively than "Parade," "Socrate" is both the logical continuation of what Satie has been about in his music during the thirty years of his career, and the most solid of the forms he has created. Under the star of the anti-impressionistic esthetic he has been following, he has managed to communicate a sincere feeling of the depth of life. There is no attempt at description, no attempt at fixing local color, in his setting of the lines from Cousin's elegant Plato. In all three fragments he has left it to the words to realize the pathos and beauty of the incidents immortalized, and striven only to sustain with infinite reserve the emotion of the poet himself.

Where Debussy would have outdone himself in depicting the tranquil scene of the cold brook and plane-tree shade that opened itself to the senses of Socrates and Phædrus during their unforgettable stroll without the walls of Athens, Satie has modestly contented himself with supplying a tender, swinging piano accompaniment that merely intensifies the effect of the language itself, and does no more. The verbal portrait of Socrates sketched by the drunken Alcibiades during the banquet is supported by a lightly moving rhythm in two-four time, broken at rare intervals by some rich brusque chords. The music of the third fragment, the narration of the incidents of the death of Socrates, does no more, with its piercing and simple and sad tones, than help communicate the grief of the beloved disciple over the end of the most sage and just of men.

But very rarely since the hour of "La Mort de Mélisande" has music more touching been produced. The deep pure sense of life that guided Satie in the selection of the three fragments for setting, remained with him when he penned his music. Those rhythms and chords and melodic figures that stir us so effortlessly stem from a clear, simple, humble feeling of what the beauty and tragedy of human life, what the grandeurs and sweetnesses of character really are. They interpret Plato for us indeed. They place us, without grandiloquence or sentimentality, in some place a little above, a little removed, from the flow of life; and even in the broken contemptible world of after-war, make us to feel again the love of the ascêsis, serenity, reserve, selflessness, undogmatism, playfulness, which the old Greek knew alone made good again the cruelties of human society. Indeed, one must go to Moussorgsky almost to find a simpler and truer statement of one who has eaten his bread in tears and knows the sad beauty of human life on this planet. Only, in the fine nude designs of "Socrate" one feels not so much the product of religious feeling, as of the wisdom of the philosophers, born again in the modesty and sanity and humbleness of a musician.

So it is no longer the clown of music we perceive first

when we think of Erik Satie. Life does strange and wondrous things to men at times. It takes from them for long years some faith and sweetness with which they came into the world; lets them wander disinherited of the strongest powers of their being; then suddenly brings them back again that which it stole, and grants them full play and enjoyment of their souls. So, in a way, has it done with Satie. The old diablerie, the old wit and spiritual bohemianism is still in him. But another side of him has waxed serenely and beautifully. And, when we gaze with the mind's eye out towards Arceuil, we see something that harmonizes entirely with Cocteau's epithet of "bon maître." We go richer for knowing that the world contains one more poet.

October, 1921.

Prize Song

IT might have been apparent to any one reading the literature sent out by the American Academy relative to its Prize of Rome in Musical Composition, that interest in the development of musical expression in the United States was not possessing with perfect singleness the minds of those to whom the making of the award had been entrusted. Quite true, the committee proposed to send the winner of its competition to Rome; there to enjoy three free years of study and toil. And, on first view, that might have seemed to betoken a sincere and unreserved devotion to the cause of music in America. But it was merely at a first glance that it could so appear to any one not entirely naïve. A second was sure to reveal only one of the committee's eyes fixed on the advancement of the art; the other wandering about over many unrelated matters. Most often, it seemed to rest on France; and there to fall with a particularly moist and benevolent ray. It was of French habits these academicians were thinking. The academy in the eternal city itself was obviously an imitation of the Villa Medici; the establishment of a musical prize destining the recipient to a three years' residence in the Italian capital smelled strongly of the brainless aping of French customs, at present the approved manner of demonstrating one's full-blooded Americanism. Provincial-mindedness was making the gesture of philanthropy; and was indeed about to bestow upon some youngling a doubtful benefit by taking him from the environment to which he was

185

Meantime, a jury sat upon the manuscripts. This
jury was composed among others, of Messrs. Walter
Damrosch, Walter Spalding, J. A. Carpenter, and W. J.
Henderson. After a very brief session of less than twenty-
four hours, the jury having satisfied itself of the value of
several works over four hundred pages in length, and of
one operatic score, rejected all eight manuscripts. None,
it was declared, showed either the creative ability or the
theoretical knowledge demanded of the competing boys.
A brief time later, it was announced that an award had
been made to Mr. Leo Sowerby, who had submitted no
work at all.

Immediately after, a new competition was announced
by the resident secretary. A typewritten circular issued
to certain young musicians fixed the term on October
thirty-first. Mr. Sowerby, so it afterward appeared, had
not been granted the three-year prize. What he had been
given was a supplementary prize consisting of a two-year
stipend. It would seem as though the young Chicagoan
had been offered the three-year prize, and had refused it
because three years seemed too long a banishment to him.

In response to the new announcement of the secretary,
one candidate, who had not competed in the first race,
telephoned the office of the academy to make sure the
competition would not close before the date set, October
thirty-first. He was assured he would run no risk of
coming late were he to work upon his manuscript up to
the hour of closure. But when the hour of closing did
come and the manuscript was presented at the office of
the secretary, the young competitor was surprised with
the announcement that the competition had been closed
over a week since, and the award made to a gentleman
from Pasadena, a Mr. Hanson, a former Damrosch pupil,
for a symphonic poem entitled "Before Dawn," or "Before

Damrosch" or something of the sort. The committee, it seems, had become suddenly very nervous. A little bird had warned them that the compositions submitted in the course of the new competition would differ in no wise in quality from those submitted in the old. They had felt positive; they had felt inwardly convinced, that there was no sense in waiting. And, like the drowning camel, they had clutched at what they considered, lunch or no lunch, to be the last straw.

It is, of course, perfectly within the rights of the responsible parties to declare a competition off because of the disappointing quality of the entries. It is perfectly within the rights of a committee of judges to award, as this one did, *hors concours* a two, three, or four-year prize to Mr. Leo Sowerby, if it is Mr. Sowerby they must have. What, however, is not within the rights of any managers of a competition is to terminate surreptitiously, as did these, a competition publicly announced; and make an award in a high-handed and arbitrary fashion. That, is a buffet to the community. In doing what it has done, the jury of the American Academy casts no positive light at all upon the meaning of the words Character, Education, and Personal Fitness, so pompously used by it. It has proved itself but part of the terrible littleness, the terrible ignorance, which has its grimy political paw on American art. Certainly, it has deprived us of any respect for the Prize of Rome, and of any hope that anything green for American culture can come out of it. We now only know that the donors are not concerned simply with the advancement of music. We can no longer have even the assurance that the competitions will be intelligently conducted. The prizeman, if he goes to three years' freedom, goes also burdened with a most doubtful honor.

November, 1921.

Bruckner

THE fire in Bruckner had free channel. Logs were not felled across its road. No neuro-watchman sprang alert as to an alarm when it began its stirring and coilings preparatory to motion, and promptly set to beating it from its course and driving it in alien directions. No haggard fear commenced running about, hissing, "Take care, this is not modern; this is not the symphony of the future; this is not what is wanted by our time; this will not free the Austrian youth and let floods of life over the sands; this is not greater than Brahms; this is not the most important form of music; this is not carrying Beethoven further than Beethoven could go." Something did not shrill, "Yonder is a man your contemporary who had done revolutionary work; make this modern, make it new and important; you must give just this nuance, you must give just that tone!" There was no floating baseless mind to interfere, to wrench the bud from its root, to commence kneading and forcing and trimming, to look into the world and get ideas and then give the musician back his substance wrapped in tight neat packages. There was the fire, only; rising, towering, finding its path; and the road before it was clear of obstructions.

What came out of Bruckner and became song of instruments is unmarred by the choking fingers of the floating mind; witness of the easiness of the passage it had into the world. Symphonies and religious services composed by him have the innocency and the largness of such stuffs as are dredged deep where life has no weakness. The music is the speech of the heart, simple and direct and

unaffected, and reverent and strong in mood. There is
no room for jewelry, for the facile, for the pretty, where
these grave and lofty tones are found. Bruckner's symphonies have scarce commenced heaving their mighty
volumes through time, before we know we are come into
the world of deep breaths and far vistas and profound
experience. We hear some one singing; singing as though
none were near to hear the song, and as though it issued
forth for its own good sake; singing out of great ecstasies
and great solitudes. The tones have their own distinct
accent, strong and uncouth and soft-colored. A horn
commences its dreamful speech over pianissimo strings;
and what comes is old, something which must have been
in every Allemand, something which must have been in
Allemanic forests long since, and that was again in Weber;
and which is new nevertheless, freighted with new solemnity and melancholy and pain.

And Bruckner's works are large in form as in conception. They bring us into contact with an elemental and
taurian strength. The lung-capacity of the man, the vast
span and breadth of his themes and thematic groups make
the majority of composers seem asthmatic. The rhythmic
hurl, curve, and freshness of his rude, lumbering, and troll-
like scherzi subjects; the Homeric delight shown by him
in ruddy sonorities, in the exuberant blasts of the reinforced brass; the cubical bulk of so many of his opening
and final movements, make it appear to the fancy as
though an elemental spirit had broken forth. Once the
slow, oxlike power is gotten in motion; once the Bruckner
orchestra begins squaring its great monoliths of tone,
then, mountainous things commence to happen. The
great gradual climaxes of the adagios of the symphonies;
the long powerfully sustained ecstasies with their wildly
and solemnly chanting trumpets, have something almost

terrible in their vehemence and amount. The great
battering-rams are slowly gotten in action. But, once
heaved forward, they crash walls down.

The man was an innocent, seeing only his own idea.
Modern music has no greater example of perfect unso-
phistication and oneness. Bruckner must have lived in
complete obliviousness of his surroundings. A sort of
rudimentary consciousness of things was there, perhaps,
sufficient to steer him through a few duties; but the
greater part of his man was walking always in the high
cathedral of his vision. Waltz-blooded Vienna could
scarce have existed for him. What rumbled and flowed
beneath his windows; what he passed through in his
courses through the streets, was vapor merely. Where a
world felt lightness of life and the decay of a state and
modern commercial tempi, there the little organist found
the walls and windows and vaulting of a cathedral nave;
and the high experiences that transformed themselves im-
perceptibly into the solemn trumpetings and ecstatic
gamuts of his unworldly musics. No brother in blank
Carthusian aisles could have paced sunken further in
prayerfulness, God-passionateness and Lenten mood, than
Bruckner through the city roads. There was the father
in heaven. There was the father in heaven, and not the
houses and the people. There was the father in heaven
who could open his robes and hang them about his child
in the cold as the walls of a woolen tent. There was no
realness in the world except the sovereign moments when
he lifted his child out of the lonely gray air into his bosom,
and held him tight with his hand till the good minute
went and the clouds of beatitude dwindled in the sad
color of the world.

Here was the paradox: the medieval God-lover, God-
embracer, in contemporary Vienna! Bruckner not only

was an innocent; he was a mystic, too. On the back of this subject of Francis Joseph's, there sat the robe of the world-estranged seer. The German mystics are his kinsmen more than are the musicians; more than is the religio-philosophical Beethoven of the ninth symphony and the "Missa Solemnis," from whom he stems; more than is the pietistic Bach, whose God-love he shared. To be sure, Bruckner remains an Austrian composer in his idiom, if not in his thought. His love for soft orchestral effects, for rich full color, links him with Schubert. Like Schubert, he speaks major in the minor keys. Indeed, there are pages of his that make him seem the most Austrian of all composers; the one least affected by Italian sweetness, and imbued most strongly with the uncontaminated racial traits. The contemporary of Wagner and Brahms and Franck, Bruckner brings to mind not so much the refinements of his own century as the uncouthness of the Allemanic tribesmen, his ancestors, who smeared their long hair with butter and brewed thick black beers. For all the magnificences of his orchestration, he remains the Upper-Austrian peasant, uncultivated, clumsy, naïve. One of his works, a Te Deum, is qualified with the adjective "Peasant"; all his work, so heavy-limbed and slow-blooded, deserves the title. The spirit of lightness, of the graceful dance, of the delicate jest, of the subtle half-statement, present in so many Austrian musicians, in Mozart, for example, is absent almost entirely from his work. Absent, too, is the gayety and charm and sweetness of Schubert. Bruckner's dance is all hoofs, all heavy springs, and drunken fury. Even the trios of his scherzi, tender, dreamy, and intermezzo-like, have a certain predominant homeliness and humbleness. The good-natured, sluggish South-German farmer dreams across his sunny land.

And yet, of course, one finds oneself setting him by the side of the religious mystics. One feels in Bruckner a completer removal from the world of objective reality, a completer tendency to consider all events purely from a psychological viewpoint, a completer habit of perceiving in the outer world merely the image of his own inner, than one finds either in the later Beethoven or in the most Mennonite pages of Bach's cantatas. It is in the company of a seer like Jacob Boehme, say, that one finds oneself instinctively placing him. In the square massive symphonies of the modern, as in the confessions of the seventeenth-century imaginer of the "centrum naturae," the "virgin Sophia," one glimpses the workings of a similar excessive transformation of the lust of the eye and the other senses into the power of mystical and almost hallucinatory vision. There are pages in the adagios of Bruckner that appear strangely akin to the records of his inner experiences left by the cobbler of Görlitz; to the experiences of the mystic marriages, the perception of fiery symbols, the progression from lugubrious depressed states through ecstasy to tranquillity. How it comes that in listening to the performances of ninety instrumentalists on their fiddles, pipes, and horns, one should enter through such forbidden doors: that, it is not easy to explain. Perhaps the cause of the strange communication lies in Bruckner's predilection for themes of a chorale or hymn-like character. It is possible that it results from the general austere and yet strangely soft and tender character of his style. His harmony is rich, solemn, stately. He delighted in the use of full, grandiose progressions of chords in the brass, through which harp music sweeps. His climaxes are slow, distended, piercing; it is possible that the solemn tones of the trombones, the sobbing of horns through pulsating chords of shrilling wind and strings, are in some measure the origin of the sensations communicated. It may be that the general character of the work, merely, predisposes one to interpret so the ecstasies. We cannot say for sure. It is doubtful whether any analysis of form, no matter how keen and scientific it may be, can arrive at elucidating these mysteries of art. And yet, we know full well that just as, in some mysterious manner, the Bruckner scherzi bring one the sensations of being in the open air, of seeing the green earth and gray sky, so, too, the Bruckner adagios gives us the sensations of an inner hallucinatory vision. The light that goes up in us from the chanting of the clear, high, loud orchestra in those movements, is not, we are somehow positive, the light that comes from the sun. It is not the light irradiated into an hundred tints by the orchestra of Debussy and the other impressionists. It is the dazzling shine that some dreaming men have suddenly seen piercing at them from out an opaque wall, or seen flooding upward at night from earth strewn thick with leaves.

A universal genius, of course, the man scarcely was. Immense though his breath, his ox-like power of sustainment, the power of his rhythmical impulse were; clear though the channel through which he gave himself to the world was; something, something important, was wanting his mentality. One feels composers dwarf in stature beside him. His muscle is greater than theirs. Yet, they are shapelier, nimbler, livelier than this lumbering man. He seems one of the Titans who sought to storm Olympus; never one of the calm gods who vanquished the frenzied Ossa-pilers.

The balance, the round development, the many sidedness which were Beethoven's, for example, never were in Bruckner, it seems. The maturity upon which solid musical culture can erect itself did not come to him.

Had Bruckner grown to the point where condensation, close interpretation, rigorous selection of material would have become a necessity to him, it is possible he might have accomplished loftier things. His rhythmical sense, his feeling for color, particularly the color of horns, was superior to the master of Bonn's. And still, his achievement is really vaguer than Beethoven's; for the reason that his sense of form remained unevolved. The corner movements of the symphonies, in particular, for in the organization of scherzi and adagios Bruckner was far more able, suffer from brokenness. They are not really organic. They heave directly into life, it is true; Bruckner's attacks are exciting and daring; he begins right in the middle of things. But when, in accord with the demands of sonata-form, he introduces his second subject, or, more exactly, his second group of subjects, one finds that apparently the trajectory has been broken and another one is commenced. It is as though the composer were commencing his work over again. Beethoven made sure that a musical logic demanded, at a certain place, the entrance of the lyrical theme. But Bruckner appears to have trusted to another logic; one perhaps not musical, for the justification of the entrance of the balancing principle. He merely sets a second piece beside the first; and leaves us to reconcile them in our minds as best we may. Not before the arrival of the development section does he commence his own "composition" of the two warring principles.

With all his faults, Bruckner remains the most neglected of symphonic composers. To be sure, there is no major symphonist, Brahms, Schubert, and Tchaikowsky excepted, whose work is not neglected by the conductors of the American orchestras. Even here in New York, where two resident and two visiting orchestras play regularly, Beethoven himself is known to the concert-public principally through five or six of his nine symphonies. Mozart is even more shabbily treated. Once, or, at the utmost, twice a year, a program holds the "Jupiter," or the g-minor symphony. The rest—is silence. But, when compared with Haydn, Mozart is as one being rushed. Ever since the departure of the terrible Dr. Muck, Haydn the symphonist remains very much in the abodes where the eternal are, and returns but seldom to the earth. The lions of the podium now rampant are very insensitive to the beauties of the adorable Haydn. They are too busy savoring to the full the subtleties of the c-major symphony of Schubert, the "From the New World" of Dvorák, to penetrate the scores of one of the most perennially fresh and delicate of composers. Smaller, though scarcely less brilliant men, fare quite as illy at their hands. Scarce ever are to be heard the symphonies of the generous and colorful Borodin. Sibelius is miserably neglected. So, too, are the modern Frenchmen. The hard, scintillant b-flat symphony of D'Indy is the rarest of visitors. That of Dukas is entirely unknown. Unknown are the works of Magnard. Meanwhile the program-makers invariably find opportunities galore for bringing before their audience the indecent exposures of Tchaikowsky.

But of all symphonists, it is Anton Bruckner who is most severely mistreated. For he wrote little besides symphonies. As composer, he is principally the composer of nine massive compositions of the sort. The body of his chamber-music is a very slight one. The chief of his compositions other than his symphonies are a few church works, the "Peasant Te Deum," and three instrumental masses. In performing him with great infrequency, the orchestral leaders are consequently effectively depriving the man of the life rightfully his, and us, the public, of the music of a weighty artist. For he lives either in the symphony-concert, or no place at all.

It is not difficult to guess why a spirit as mighty as Bruckner's should be kept, like a genie of the "Arabian Nights," corked in a jar by the confraternity of musicians. The musicians, for their part, harp on Bruckner's grotesqueries. There are two composers on whom musicians are most stupid, Moussorgsky, and the Austrian mystic. Every day one meets some solemn performing person who informs one that Moussorgsky could not compose; and one has but to mention the name of Bruckner to him, too, to hear remarks equally inane. Bruckner "was a madman"; did he not most childishly dedicate his ninth symphony "Zum lieben Gott"? To be sure, the dedication makes one smile. But then, Bruckner had presented his eighth to His Imperial and Royal Apostolic Majesty Francis Joseph I, Emperor of Austria and Apostolic King of Hungary, etc., etc.; and for a devout Austrian there was only one person to whom one might fittingly present a ninth, the Francis Joseph beyond the clouds. Moreover, the "madman" had taken the opening phrase of Isolde's Liebestod and fugued it! And though tomes have been written to prove that several centuries before Bruckner other composers lifted the same theme from Wagner and fugued it, the musicians must have their little joke.

No, it is the confraternity that is grotesque. If "Boris" is withdrawn from the repertory of the Metropolitan Opera House, to the applause of all the Henry T. Fincks; if the conductors of the metropolitan orchestras neglect above all others the symphonies of Anton Bruckner, it is not for the reason the Russ and the Upper-Austrian could not make music. It is for the reason that the rarefied air

that blows through the works of both demands lungs
stouter and hearts higher than the musical unions and the
company of the conductors can plentifully supply. One
can scarcely be a practicing musician and do the little
jobs the public demands musicians do, and still feel life
with the altitude and the solemnity and reverence with
which these men felt it. The world would first have to be
lost to one.

November, 1921.

Saint-Saëns

THE music of the late Camille Saint-Saëns has something
of the quality of an official music to the Third Republic.
Elegant, frosty, ironic, it nevertheless, savors in some
strange way of the official art. Where the academically
brushed portraits of Presidents are exposed on the walls
of galleried Versailles; where, above the panel-work of
public buildings classic-garmented Peace, Justice, and
Fraternity gracefully bear sheaves of corn, scales, and
infants, after the manner of the school of the Beaux Arts,
there are its cousins. We in this land do not readily recognize in this urbanity and lightness the imprint of
official-mindedness. We are more used to a hippopota-
mus, a Nicholas Murray Butler quality, in the intelli-
gences of our "friends of order." Doubtless, Saint-Saëns
would have been most displeased had any one pointed out
to him the affinity between his work and that of the academical painters of France, of the academical authorities
in America. It would not have been until there had
reëntered his mind the haunting thought that the criticism
was inspired by German jealousy of his achievement, that
he would have found any consolation. He conceived of
himself, most indubitably, as Voltairean and disabused, a
ray of French clarity, reason, and irony incorporated.
He loved smooth and elegant effects in his music. He was
a man of the world even in his rhythms. At moments,
particularly at those moments when he was not engaged
in engineering an opera of his composition on the stage
of the Théâtre National de la Musique, he was informed
by a sense of the futility of human effort, and doubtless

thought of himself as a new ecclesiast. Such a one would scarcely have been deceived by the pretended urbanites of our academic Castigliones. He would have viewed without enthusiasm the whiskers of Professor Brander Matthews; have perceived in Mr. Paul Elmer More the imperfect clubman; seen in Professor Irving Babbitt the Presbyterian minister manqué. And still, despite sparkle and Candidian disillusionment, his was essentially the official mind; and the minds of those in every country who fear growth and departure are only superficially dissimilar.

The immense body of work left behind him by the indefatigable little trotter was the outcome of a sincere orientation in musical composition checked by an apparent terror of untrodden mental paths. Side by side with Saint-Saëns, there lived and labored aplenty professors whose orientation was not of any intensity; we would never find ourselves mistaking their dull music for his agreeable and oftentimes amusing work. The penmanship of Saint-Saëns invariably gives pleasure. We are gratified by the neatness with which he manages his effects. There is clearness and lightness in the texture of his music; and when we are not irritated with the triviality of the material and the coldness of the informing breath, we are tickled by the charm of his surfaces. The man had elegant musical manners always. At times, a sort of cool and fresco-like loveliness pervades his marmoreal melodies, his snappy rhythms and sugary ornamentation. Often, he is delightfully Frenchy, *bal musette;* his ideas have gayness and irresponsibility; and his music smiles with the glee of one who is amusing himself perfectly with his work. A living impulse was somewhere in him. In the midst of conventional, salon-spirited, superficial pieces, there show their heads for

him. The eye which looks at, was very active; the eye
which looks into, weak. And, knowing styles superficially
only, and not understanding the element of necessity
which gave life to them, he never came to any clear comprehension of the problem of expression. The personal
manners of the great musicians must have seemed always
as ingenious masks, to be assumed and doffed at will. All
his life, we find him amusing himself with the imitation
of various styles of composition; and mixing them with a
kind of vulgar insensibility. One of his piano-concerti
commences in a severe, contrapuntal and Bach-like
manner; then, later, in the trio, skips and cavorts in the
fashion of Offenbach. There was nothing incongruous for
Saint-Saëns in this juxtaposition of mysticism and skirt-
dance. He assimilated at other times with like facility
and superficiality the styles of Wagner and Berlioz and
Handel, of Lulli and Rameau and Byrd. His "Symphonie avec Orgue" is based on the prose of the "Dies
Irae." All his life he was looking outside himself; exposing himself to exotic influence, searching out new color,
new stimulus. He himself was always traveling from one
climate to another; and his mind trotted over the globe
even more than his body, and toured in the present and in
the past. The immense list of his compositions includes
Algerian suites, Breton and Auvergnac rhapsodies, Per-
sian songs, Egyptian concerti, Biblical oratorios, African
fantasies, Chinese operettas, Portuguese barcarolles,
Danish, Russian, and Arabian caprices, music for Greek
tragedies and Shakespearean chronicles, preludes and
fugues of the eighteenth century. But there is no depth
in this welter of color. It resembles the sketch-book of
an amateur aquarellist. The world entered the man
through his head only. The inner sensitive substance he
never exposed. Nothing he wrote is without charm; but

nothing is warm and moving and truly personal. The profile is old and dull. As a flippant young critic once put it, "M. Camille Saint-Saëns is less a personality than he is an impersonality." His music seems a bewildering and slightly glaciated echo of Mendelssohn; and Mendelssohn himself was a good deal of an echo, a Saint-Saëns of the fiery 'thirties. For both men were concerned with making their feelings conform, guarding against their natural impulses. And feeling is after all the carrier of personality and of life.

Like the utterances of the academicians, the music of Saint-Saëns subtly bids experimentation desist. Superficially, of course, the art of this musician, so airy and dilettantishly brilliant, has little affair with the French State. Saint-Saëns composed neither an ode to Reason, a tone-poem on the battle of Valmy, nor a tripartite symphony entitled Liberty, Equality, Fraternity. But, essentially, his work is inspired by the spirit that serves well the powers of state. With disarming lightness, but with no little cynicism, it insinuates abnegation of personality. Contours bid development cease. Forms suggest deification of past experience, disdain of the unaccepted, the untried, the unborn. You stand chilled and disturbed, doubtful of your own convictions, unsure of your own desires, belittled and wearied, quite as though you were assisting at a ceremony over which President Nicholas Murray Butler presided. This music, too, makes the power of feeling in you, the unborn worlds to which it performs midwifery, appear the black devil. So it assists materially the powers of state that are eager to lull the unsatisfied sense of justice, the unsatisfied sense of truth, the unsatisfied need of creation in men; eager to smother all revolutionary impulse of any sort, and thus preserve themselves in unchallenged power.

attractive with age. It seems highly doubtful whether it can maintain itself in the future. The incident of his death, no doubt, will inspire a number of our wearier conductors with the idea of commemorative revivals. A certain class of virtuosi will persist for years, perhaps, in playing his concerti, so rich in opportunities for the musical gymnast. But it is personal style which preserves the work of art against the warfare of time. It is to the men who fought the conventions and registered their own individualities, that the world is drawn back from time to time. M. Camille Saint-Saëns, however, wrote mountainously and added not an iota to the art of music. Something in him had chosen between life and death; and we find no tears to shed over the fact that his work seems destined for the bourne which he elected for it.

December, 1921.

The Visit of Richard Strauss

ONCE more, we have seen Richard Strauss in America.
Once more, we have been permitted to glimpse his sleepy
and peevish and slightly disappointed expression of face;
been permitted to watch him drift gracefully onto the
podium on a New York stage and drift gracefully off
again; to follow the swimming play of his baton at the end
of an arm that might have sported a bracelet; to hear him
execute indifferently well with a look of martyrdom the
accompaniments to his songs. Once again, we have been
given, under his direction, a sort of Strauss Festival.
According to the careful computation of the critic of the
New York *World*, Strauss during his recent visit gave
upward of forty concerts in America; appeared in nine-
teen cities; played eleven times in New York; conducted,
or played the accompaniment of sixty of his compositions. Nearly everything written by him for orchestra
was performed. Not even the violin concerto and "Mac-
beth" were permitted to sleep undisturbedly their justly
merited slumber. The dance of Salomé was played twice
at one concert in the Metropolitan Opera House, where
once it had so disagreeably shocked the boxholders.
And, once again, Richard Strauss has gone out of the
port of New York in the general direction of Munich,
Garmisch and Vienna, carrying with him at least three
coins of the realm.

Still, between the second going and the earlier, there
was a notable unlikeness. When Strauss departed the
country not quite eighteen years since, no universal

handkerchief-waving, but a loud and absurd scandal blared after his vanishing coattails. Strauss, it was declared, had degraded music. To be sure, Richard Strauss had been degrading music a long while; ever since, indeed, some good folk had perceived in "Don Juan" the musical depiction of the sort of establishment whose existence is generally ignored in polite society, and in "Till Eulenspiegel" the representation of pothouse scenes. But, on this occasion, the degradation had been a more exquisite one. The premier German composer of his hour, the heir therefore, to Mozart and Beethoven and Wagner, Strauss, it was raged, had dragged the heavenly muse Cecilia through the disreputable aisles of drygoods and commercialdom. By performing his works in the auditorium atop a department-store, Strauss had lowered his art to the "level" of department-stores. All Olympus with the thunder shook, and the clever person suggested that the composer name his next tone-poem Wanamakeriana.

This year, no furore followed the departing figure of the descendant of Liszt and beerbrewer Pschorr. But it was not for the reason that Strauss eschewed his old disreputable haunts off Astor Place and frequented chastely the Metropolitan Opera and Carnegie Hall, those temples of pure art, that glory spoke where previously blame had scolded. Doubtless, Richard II might have conducted again at Wanamaker's and played not only Strauss, but Mozart and Beethoven and Wagner, and yet reaped no whirlwind. For still it moves.—We are no longer as certain as once we were that it degrades music to bring her into department-stores. We no longer see the Metropolitan Opera and Carnegie Hall standing on a plane far above your ordinary Broadway or Forty-second street bazaar. On the contrary, we feel the quality of the goods

sold in certain of the latter superior to those for sale in
the former. True, many of the department-stores carry
modern and machine-made goods of a poor quality. But
at their worst, these objects are no more vulgar or de-
pressing than the sort of performances familiar to our
red and brown upholstered sacred groves. And at least,
you can sit upon Grand Rapids; you can keep yourself
warm under an alice-blue comforter stuck with pink
rosettes. But what can you do with a symphony conducted by Stransky? Or a performance of "Die Tote
Stadt" or "Mona Lisa"?

No, it was not for the reason that Strauss trod in the
ways of convention, that his second visit ended under
the sunset of respectability. Over his second voyage to
these western waters there shone the sign of an unofficial
conciliatory embassy. And that fact would have prevented another Wanamaker scandal, even if one had
threatened to rise; and did help make his trip a many-
sided success. It may be that the impulse of concilia-
tion was secondary only in bringing about the visit of
Strauss; that it was chiefly for the purpose of collect-
ing money and reviving the fainting interest in his works
that the composer came. But it was as a sort of unofficial ambassador of German life that he was received
by numbers of people here; and that determined the
effect of his action. It was as a representative of what
still manages to live in German bodies that the worthies
of City Hall welcomed him in their fashion, a very few
days after they had extended a like welcome to Foch. It
was as such that the crowds that filled even the aisles
of Carnegie Hall during Strauss's first concert applauded
him. People came to hear the music, it is true. People
came to see with their own eyes the wonder-working
magician of the orchestra. People also came for the

purpose of being able to prefix their remarks to those to
whom they wished on the morrow and the day after to
sell some bonds, with a "cultured" account of a Strauss
concert, a sort of variation of the eternal "I've just read
such an interesting article in the 'New Republic' "; and
thus prepare a little more favorably the entrance of the
statement, "I've got some awfully cheap stuff which'll
certainly interest you." But, most of all, we are assured,
the audience was composed that night of men and women
glad with all their hearts that there had been made possible for them some act whereby they might purge their
breasts of all the stupid hatred called up in them by the
morale of an unpopular war. It was composed of people
who came because they sensed secretly that in assisting
they would once more become free to go out to everything good in music as once they had gone out to it. It
was composed of people who came in mute protest against
all the lawless bullying which had been inflicted upon
them in the face of a law-power too corrupt to protect
dissident minorities; who came to protest against the
weakness in themselves which had permitted howling
muckerdom to snatch in the name of humanity their
innocent pleasures away from them. And if Strauss was
still able, after his reception at the hands of the immortal
Hylan, after all the years which have passed over him
since he was a poet, to feel anything at all, something of
what surcharged the atmosphere in crowded Carnegie
Hall that evening must have pervaded him. He, too,
must for a moment have looked within, and felt there,
for all his self-righteous rage over the blows struck the
culture of middle Europe, an humility before the human
self ever outraged and betrayed by the human being.
And once again, he must have marveled at the tragic
absurdity of an existence in which the chief actors at

almost regular intervals, fall upon their very selves in
wolfish destructivity.

It is not Strauss the person alone that has gotten, after
the lapse of the eighteen years, a new face. Time has
altered his music, too. In 1904, Richard Strauss was, in
Huneker's phrase, an "anarch of art." He was a sort
of musical antichrist writing forbidden and occult and
world-tumbling things for grand orchestra; pulling the
white beard of God with his harmonies; initiating his
audiences into satanic and wicked philosophies through
tone; stirring hell-kitchen cauldrons in his fast-playing
band. The very thought of the programs of his symphonic poems made one dizzy. He proposed to set one
in the boots of an archrogue; to make one experience
death; dance with Nietzsche the monster-philosopher;
collide as superman with the cosmic riddle; step over the
prostrate crowds in the stride of the hero; lift the curtain of the alcove where married people sleep. It was
like nothing so much as flying off the battlements of the
tower of Babel to pursue vain war with Heaven. One
knew what Huneker meant when he wrote that Strauss
composed "with the pen of beyond good and evil." One
saw with delicious shudders the unforgivable in sin heave
over the horizon. And in performance, the music was
infinitely bewildering, infinitely exciting. It went so fast,
faster even than Wagner. Violins spiralled into the deeps
of the firmament. The noise stepped out and stunned
you. You could never rest quite sure as to what was
supposed to be happening; whether Till was upsetting
the apple-carts of the market-women or making a long
nose at the professors, or hearing the judge pronounce
sentence against him; whether Don Juan was making
love to the Countess or to Anna or to Zerlinchen;
whether the orchestra was painting the infancy, adoles-

cence, or old age of the dying man. Was that religion, or was it science, that was being discarded by humanity in its attempt to reconcile inhuman nature with man's metaphysical mind? Was the hero writing now, "Tod und Verklärung" or "Trum durch die Dämmerung"; was the uncle saying "Just like mama"; was the clock striking six in the evening or six in the morning? Were Herr und Frau Dr. Richard Strauss connubially embracing, or were they throwing the breakfast dishes at each other's heads, or presaging their youngster's grandiose future? Positive, one could never be. And when one did succeed in following the program, sonorous and brilliant passages set everything in one glittering and chiming. The plangent trumpets in the finale of "Don Quixote" were the voice of lashing, howling, mocking disillusionment. That, was the iron tread of the hero as he strode over Europe with the swing of Rodin's walking man. That, was the sun on the banging timpani of "Zarathustra." The singing horns and violins of Don Juan's feast painted the scene one intended some day to live.

Long before the interruption of the war, these thundercolors had paled from Strauss. Another image, still undeterminate, was coming to occupy the place held by the former "anarch of music." Then, the war dropped the curtain over his figure for a couple of years. And when it rose again, on the Strauss festival, the new image was there; a transformation indeed! The new Strauss that produced himself to our eyes while his orchestral compositions passed before us in review, was the opposite almost of the antichrist of tone. From the most troubling, the composer has become one of the most comfortable, amusing, relaxing of musicians. The concerts of his work given by him were the most delightful of light evening entertainments; the most splendid of pastimes.

They were luminous frescoes of sleepy, lovely, charming sound; passages of opalescent light which one drank with a smile pretending they were wines. Never was one exalted or thrilled by this music. The music seemed no more "modern" than that of Schumann. One was bored, sometimes; much of the stuff was dreadfully dull; the solo-violin and the Brobdingnagian battle-scene in "Heldenleben," the first large section of "Sinfonia Domestica" were exasperatingly empty. More often, one found oneself in a state of childish delight over the sweet and pricking things going on down in the orchestra. It was all like a marvelously amusing game in which one joined for a while, and which one might quit again at will. A good time was had by all. The Philadelphia Orchestra played suavely and brightly as it rarely plays under the baton of Mr. Stokowski. Frau Schumann sang with a gift of herself, with a goodness, a pure loveliness of tone, not often heard in New York. At the end of these concerts, one put up one's coat-collar in a pleasant humor, and went away contented, whistling one of the composer's fetching tunes.

It was a great musician that Richard Strauss once more proved himself to be. But it was a great musician, in a restricted sense of the word. The tone poems of this child of Munich are marvelous things—for the ear only. Little has been written for orchestra that can match these rich-sounding works in pure sonority. They are fantasias of orchestral language of a brilliance that still overwhelms. It is doubtful whether any composer has better understood the instruments of the band than this man; has had a more voluptuous feeling for the noises of brass and strings, the windy beauty of the horns, the velvet of reeds; reveled more luxuriously in these bright, high-pitched sounds. It is doubtful whether any one has had a nicer sense of the purely orchestral possibilities, of the general range of the instruments, of the beautiful tapestry-like interplay of these sonorities. He has written passage upon passage of marvelous networks of timbres and colors, rich, savorous, and dense. The great, many-stranded middle section of the Sinfonia; the shimmering, high-fluted introduction to what Mr. Deems Taylor has so cutely called the Übermenschen-walzer; the poisonously entrancing reeds in the dance of the Seven Veils, bewitch us over and over again with their sheer iridescent loveliness. It is a marvelous sensuality this man possesses; a virtuosic gift for orchestration like that of D'Annunzio for prose, of Rubenstein for piano-playing.

In this many-hued stream of sound, you bathe as you might bathe in a river of perfumed vapor. You issue from it neither touched nor warmed nor refreshed. The music of Strauss has very little to give the mind. You cannot listen to these works and be moved. Life is somehow not strongly in them. They stir nothing deep in you. They nourish no high tremulous sense of beauty. There is a sort of lusty abundance in some of them, in "Don Juan" particularly; but this, too, wears a curiously fictitious look. For, though Strauss has a marvelous sensuous gift, his gift remains a superficial thing. In spite of his wizard-like control over the means of expression he has very few striking ideas. His thematic material wants distinction, wants quality. There is something always a little common, a little wanting in edge and incisiveness, in his melodic line. It is Strauss to some degree; but it is also a little everybody's music. Whenever he ceases being clever and bitter-ironic; whenever he tries to sing, to express a sustained emotional state, he lapses very quickly into a not very refined ancestral German idiom, a sort of facile and plebeian melodiousness which is ever so near the German heart. One finds it at its worst in Korngold. It is not at all at its best in the master. Were it merely a German equivalent for the folksong that is to be found in the music of the Russian nationalist school, there would be no cause of complaint. But, alas, it tastes much less of the simple folk than of the half-educated middle classes with their taverns, männerchöre, operettas, and beer. To be sure, Strauss manages to clothe these plebeian generalities in most magnificent dress; to press out of them, thanks to his amazing contrapuntal technique, the last drop of emotional possibility which they contain. But one is always conscious that the musical table is loaded with foods and flagons of doubtful quality.

Moreover, the greater number of Strauss' works want form. With the exception of "Tod und Verklärung" and perhaps "Till Eulenspiegel," his tone poems seem fragmentary; he wanders through the greater number of his songs, too. No great inner structure carries them taut from commencement to finish. Rather more, they seem a series of short breaths arbitrarily riveted together. The bow was not taut when this man set out to compose "Zarathustra" or "Don Quixote" or "Ein Heldenleben." The works begin with triumphant impulse. But before many minutes have elapsed, one gets the sense that Strauss did not have any strong feeling of the direction in which he was going when he set out so bravely; and that the extension of the form is the result only of a secondary conception. Handsome passages do ensue—the vigil in "Don Quixote," the love scene and the brave return of the original theme in "Heldenleben"; the marvelously densely woven middle-section in the "Sinfonia Domestica." But as soon as these are over, the musical Sahara returns.

And at the conclusion, we have the baffled sense of having heard a number of not clearly connected fragments; not the great inner satisfaction that comes through having been moved through thick matter in an unbroken course.

In Strauss, it would seem, we have again to do with one of those individuals in whom sensuality is an unconnected thing, cut off from the rest of the being. In those individuals whose senses are ports wide open upon the world, apertures through which the world can enter whole into the heart, the idea is always to some degree present in the sensation. The sensation comes freighted with an abstract dimension. The thought is inextricably commingled with the object present to the thinker. Strauss' emotional schemes, on the contrary, seem always to have come into him a little separate and distinct from the musical stuff. Because he cannot feel directly; because it is impossible for him to go into himself, and there receive life directly, something in him is always busy externalizing his ideas, showing him them from an oblique and indirect angle. A musician, his conceptions commence as something always a little extra-musical; not as purely musical idea. His ideas seem to originate in him first as abstract, as literary conceptions, to which the music later adds itself. But although musical invention subsequently marries itself to the abstract, the literary conception, the idea and the musical form remain always a little apart. It is necessary for the music that a program explain it, for as music it cannot stand alone.

Hence, we cannot longer see Richard Strauss standing among the musical creators. Not even "Tod und Verklärung" can quite succeed in keeping him there. What he has achieved wants too much the form, the inner life, which makes the genuine work of art. There is marvelous imitation of nature in his poems and in "Elektra." There is mordant self-ridicule and instrumental farce in "Till Eulenspiegel" and "Don Quixote." His symphonies are perhaps the most brilliant of orchestral arabesques. But innocent directness of expression, the simplicity which the technique-poor Moussorgsky had so abundantly, he has never captured; and all his king's horses and all his king's men are as feathers balanced against that pure poetic gift. It is with the virtuosi he must stand. And with the virtuosi he must face the inevitable knife which goes through the world cutting down those things which men make not in the depths of their own beings, but somewhere outside themselves.

January, 1922.

The Ornstein Double Sonata

THE themes which spring forth from the unbreaking
gray plinth of sound in the Ornstein two-piano sonata,
fling themselves out like running reliefs and merge and
make way again for other outrushing material, belong
to the race of the young composer's vital ideas. These
jerking, wailing, clanging motifs are not of the sort of
the sweet sugary ghosts, scions of a violent house become
soft and indulgently melancholy and prettily oriental,
which appeared in the 'cello sonatas and pianoforte sona-
tinas composed by him a few years since. Theirs is the
strong blood, the blunt power and sinister coloration
which sounded in the fierce and doleful preludes and
impressions, moods, and sonatas, which announced another
composer had been born lurid modern life. The angry
protest against sweet, easy, lying rhythms is in them. The
beat of the city is in the immense dark crashes, the violent masses of complex tone. They run swift with
the leaping modern mind.

Into the glittering metallic stream of the new work
Ornstein has poured, in some measure, his own timeliness
and spiritual complexity. The many planes of his personality, the many shaping influences which bore on him,
mirror themselves therein. Themes recall the arias and
recitatives of synagogue cantors that must have come into
the child with the first light of the world, and echo the
subtle elaborate cadences, the oriental monotony, of the
ritual chants. Themes recall the street-songs, part Slavic,
part Jewish, of the towns of the Pale; vulgar tunes of

the working people and the nurse-girls, scraps of the tavern and the road. Themes speak violent sensuality drowned in black, violent passion submerged and become fear, become hideous weariness and depression, become the lurid blue and black of the East Side of New York. Certain appear which seem like raucous cries of suddenly felt steely power, the stamps, the gestures, the whistles of one who would represent with his own person the might of machinery; the response, part joyous, part frenetic to the mud and the steam-sirens, the derricks and the towering hulks of the great ports: West Street, the Thames ocean-docks, Hamburg. Others are like the noises of the human breast deep down where it is scarcely longer human, beastly hysterical howlings one does not want to know present in the subcellar of the body. And others, still, break out in unbridled wild dance; crow, whistle, and gong like a college of Chinese on a holiday; flame with the warm, quick-jetting Jewish blood when it overcomes fear and gives itself joyously and abandonedly.

Perhaps not every ounce of Ornstein's young giant-hood was pressing upon his material when he composed his double sonata. The capacity for deep feeling latent in the twenty-six year old composer is not completely exhausted in the work, it seems. There is something in him that has the crude black power of the engines and the piles of industrialism; and that power was not fully given in to and released by him in this piece. The double sonata, significantly, enchants the sense more deeply than it touches the heart. The door was only partly opened. Nevertheless, the music possesses a beauty which has never before been manifested in his productions. In it, there is a coming together of many elements never before fused. The thematic material has been forcefully wrenched, submitted to a superior and single conception. It is a little as though motives which had never before worked together, had suddenly timidly conjoined their palms, and begun an harmonious and flowing movement. They are related to one another. They necessitate each other's presence. They produce each other with grace. They still dance with angular tic-like jerks; whimper and wail in Jewish egoistic over-indulgence in grief; stampede like herds of terrified locomotives madly clanging their bells; proclaim passionately romantic tragedy and romantic pride. But it is as if an alchemist with his virtuous stone had touched many disparate, separate black objects, and transfused them to a single dark lustrous metal. Relativity has made them clear and winged and light. A dense stream of rich sound pours from the two vibrating instruments; a flood yellow-gray as the warm voluptuous winter sky over New York. Climax upon climax is churned. Ornstein at last has produced a sizeable object with an authentic life of its own.

For the first time, it seems, Ornstein has out-topped his medium, and done his work outside as well as inside himself. For the first time, he seems to have been more deeply interested in the thing before him than in himself before the thing; and perceived his stuff as a thing separate from himself, and possessing a design absolutely its own. Genius, we know, was in him from the moment he wrote the "Dwarf Suite." The city world had in some manner entered through the ear of this lad, for whom any two notes of the pianoforte were under the stress of necessity to be combined. But it must have been the state of production which interested him more than the objects produced; the volcanic eruption of his own emotions and fears more than the medium through which he was ostensibly releasing himself. The result, he never

saw with objective eye. That, is demonstrated by the
work itself. Biting and high instants of music occurred
in nearly everything which came out of him, once he had
found his voice. There is always the beginning of human
expression in his pieces. At some moments, matter takes
form and the instrument chants seraphically. One re-
members for such a moment some not very successful
variations of the favorite Volga boatman song. For,
after three movements in which nothing is firmly laid
hold upon and everything goes through the clutching
fingers, there comes a fourth that is a sumptuous
throbbing thing, a dream of rich textures tremblingly
felt of. But the greater number of these works, those in
smaller as well as in larger form, want rhythm. The
logic felt by the composer does not really exist in the
structures. Dazzling and powerful in certain of their
aspects, they want vital organization. One does not feel
the double pull in them, the counterplay that makes the
life of art. The fragments are really unmarried, separate,
unmoving. Even in the more successful of the briefer
pieces, the famous "Three Moods," for example, there is a
sort of fatiguing monotonousness. The King of France
marches up the hill; but he does not march down again;
and art commences with the relation of at least two
elements.

With the double sonata, this, the period of the ado-
lescence of a distinguished artist ends. The composition
comes to us in testimony of the fact that an imagination
has begun to struggle loose, has commenced timidly
functioning; that a man has come to feel the complexness
of life, to know the not-I as well as the ego. Rhythm,
real movement, is in this work; and out of it there comes
to us the feeling of the impersonal, impalpable, superior
thing we know as beauty. For Ornstein has grappled

with large and rebellious matter his own size, and achieved
with it a solid if not entirely elegant and athletic form.
An inner shape defines itself through the clamoring
material. The three movements, one lengthy, two briefer,
stand fairly well defined against one another, complement
one another. The thematic material in each is distinct,
and yet a certain homogeneity obtains throughout the
work. A strong, not very subtle, but clearly defined line is
maintained throughout. It will be seen that the composer
has developed his own feeling for distinguished and net
forms from study of Scriabine; the complex César Franck
and Florent Schmitt quintets have also taught him much,
have given him a model of richness of workmanship. To
be sure, Ornstein, though he rivals his masters in opulence
of material, is still constrained by the demands of form.
A certain rigidity is to be observed in his themes. Musicians might feel he has not exhausted all the possibilities
of development latent in the rich stuffs. Nothing is more
certain than that Ornstein, for all his immense dramatic
power, is far from possessing the miraculous technique of
development displayed, say, by Ernest Bloch. Still, the
man is obedient to his inner voice. Every page of the
sonata reveals him struggling towards a technique fit
his personality. A not very refined, but nevertheless not
unrespectable solidity of construction has already been
obtained. If the form of the new sonata is not specially
deep and distended, the movements nevertheless hang
well together. In the first movement, which is dubbed
by the composer "Fantasy," but which is indeed an essay
in the binary form, having an introduction, two thematic
groups, a development section, a restatement of the second
group, and a coda shaped of material drawn from the
first, the two sets of themes, the one more vertical and
harmonic, the second more horizontal and melodic, are

well contrasted. The material is in several marked instances surprisingly well deployed, the composer inventing, with an often marvelously rich fantasy, as he proceeds. The movement may, however, be slightly prolix. It appears possible that Ornstein, in revulsion from fragmentariness, brevity of wind, and poverty of construction, had been a trifle too thoughtlessly generous, had crowded into his bag a little more than it quite conveniently might contain. The second and third movements are less ambitious, and less replete. Of all, the weary, slumberous second is surely the best cast, perhaps because, in its slightness and simplicity, it offered the composer a comparatively small problem. A three-part song, with certain important extensions, it seems one of those shapes that happen very quietly on the days when life is all mountain-crest. The third movement, a rondo, possesses a good deal of the foursquareness of the second. Less rich and less subtly worked out than the first, it is perhaps the most powerful of all three. One feels a massive inner form. Simple effects are obtained by the sheer and un-bridged contrasts of violently rhythmical prancing passages with pianissimo lamenting and lugubrious pages.

What gives the work its highest esthetic value is its magnificently pianistic properties. If Ornstein's strong nature is still a little constrained by the problems of composition, it is released in the language he writes. He is still something of a boy in his form; but the degree to which his inventions lie within the medium of his instrument places him in the very forefront rank of those who are developing to-day the art of tone. The two pianos which stood together on the platform of Æolian Hall the night the double sonata was performed seemed strange and many-throated black animals. It was not the circumstances that they were played by two diabolos of piano-

forte-playing like Miss Leginska and the composer himself, that might be made accountable for the fine metallic
clangor, the infinitely subtle timbres, they gave forth.
These were produced by the profound sensitivity of the
composer to the media. The figuration, the color-con-
trasts, the actual placing and breaking of the total masses,
was done with a happy, sure, and easy hand. Ornstein
possesses deep intuition of the nature of his instrument.
Everything which he writes, sounds. The writing makes
the two instruments give forth not the crushed richness
of one piano doubled, but of one piano tripled or even
quadrupled. And yet the immense silver volume of tone
was never thick, never muddy. The two pianos balanced
each other, strengthened each other with their sharply
conflicting rhythms and tonalities. Together, they did
terrible and wondrous things; howled like beasts in the
wilderness when the sap mounts; clattered like "golden
jewels down a golden stair"; arabesqued "chop-sticks";
were pounding rhythms; were dark, velvety, lugubrious;
wailed like mourners at the wall in Jerusalem; were like
anvils from which flew solid metal sparks as the strange
intervals of the Ornstein melodies sped and rocketed upward.

Because of the piano-sense developing in him, Ornstein
to-day seems to us to be on the verge of becoming a
member of the line of composers that moves from
Frédéric Chopin through Aleksander Scriabine and onward into gray unknown regions. Despite a distinctly
limited range of ideas, he seems the latest of these orgiastic
and solitary figures who confide imperiously to the solo
instrument par excellence their pride and grief and love
of magnificences. Of course, it remains possible that his
virtuosity may still impede him, and approach him always
more to Rubinstein than to Scriabine. So strong a sensu-

ous gift, so much facility, makes it very easy for the possessor to remain always something of an improviser. There is still enough of a suspicion of plebeian flatfootedness, enough of a want of aristocratic distinction of line, in the double sonata, to trouble even Leo Ornstein's most fervent enthusiasts. But one begins to breathe up. The tide that sweeps through the new work moves from a different zone. It transports us forth again into the gray horizonless open where it is good to swim. Out here, we know how unhappy we were in the locked baylet where much of the very finest of new music had left us. It is the wave and the wind and the pounding heart that give us life. It was for this battle that we were born. And we will not believe that, once having so swiftly swirled off its man, it will readily let him resist being carried ever farther out into the godlike open.

February, 1922.

Gozzi and Prokofieff

In Serge Prokofieff's opéra-bouffe, the mask Trouffaldino comes to amuse the hypochondriac son of the King of Clubs, and fails: not because he is not comical, but because the Prince is incurably atrabilious. Now, the audience which heard "L'Amour des Trois Oranges" the night the Chicago Opera Association performed it for the first time in New York, was able to laugh. It did laugh at all of the stage-business which was really comical. And if it found itself unamused by the work as an entirety, it was for the reason that, contrary to the instance enacted on the stage, Trouffaldino Prokofieff proved himself far less witty and diverting a musician than he intended being when he set out to make operatic audiences shed their solemnity and guffaw over an opéra-bouffe. The invention of the young Russian composer again showed itself incapable of meeting adequately the situation he creates for it when he essays extended and sustained composition. Few conditions have been more favorable to its production; few conditions it will ever meet, it seems, can more cordially invite it, than those which surrounded it when he set about fleshing the delicious and ironical *commedia dell' arte* of old Carlo Gozzi. Prokofieff is in temper entirely unlyrical. His moods are impish, Puckish, exasperated, sarcastic. He writes, it appears from his productions, most often in humors half playful half irritable; scrubs out upon the pianoforte little angry marches, acidulous badinage, scornful fleeting signs of the thumb and nose, all sorts of impish suggestions. He is his own

228

butt, most probably, a good portion of the time. One sees him sitting much-admired among the persons and furnishings of the mauve salon world; and if at certain moments, as in "Tales of the Old Grandmother," he is a little dreamy and poetical, at others more numerous, he is bored and self-satirical and in rare bad humor. A certain broad sense of the comedy of orchestral instruments he possesses, without dispute. He knows, for instance, how to make the bassoon, the clown of the band, grunt funny if not quite subtle noises. True, his comedy has elements of musical slapstick. But once one finds its level, it can tickle.

And the dry and mocking fairy-tale of the irresponsible old Venetian offered Prokofieff a golden opportunity of producing his Puckish, mocking, grotesque strain to fullest advantage. Half the work had already been done for him. He had the rarest of clothes-horses upon which to drape his fabric. Even in the almost undeveloped scenario-form in which it has descended to us, Gozzi's "L'Amore delle Tre Melerancie" remains a masterly bit of romantic irony. It is self-satire of the soul more nimble and easy than any to be found in all the stage-pieces of Tieck, Brentano and other of the ironists of the romantic group. Transcendental philosophizing does not weigh it to earth. It is not literary, but born within the framework of the stage. And still, your incurably subjective dreamer, conscious that the reality of all things is only his own interest in them, bored with his subjectivity and nevertheless unable to escape from his prison, might go far before he found another machine better able to release him through laughter. Here, as in all of Gozzi's fairy-plays, the soul shows itself with infinite slyness as phantasmal as the spectacle of life which it has conjured up for its own diversion,

demonstrates itself the dupe of its own silly fantasies.
The nurse's tale which serves for plot divides the specta-
tor between naïve interest and sophisticated mockery; he
sees himself bewitched by colors which he himself has projected onto the screen of the universe by means of the un-
extinguishable magic-lantern in his own breast. The mari-
onette, the playing-card souls of the protagonists whom no
poetical projection on the part of the author has brought
to life, continue the schism. They, too, let the sleep-walker
perceive himself as he walks in sleep. The presence upon
the stage of the five stock masks of the immemorial Italo-
Latin clown comedy, Tartaglia, Trouffaldino, Brighella,
Pantaleone, and Esmeraldine further points the sly self-
satire. For are not these creatures immortal beings who
act in plays which they themselves improvize and which
they are at liberty at any instant to terminate? Again,
the continuous invasion of the scene by the "absurdities"
and other players representing that portion of the self
which watches its own frenetic activities and produces
a world for its own amusement, turns the laugh always
inward. Like the Hans Wurst of one of Tieck's farces,
these curious creatures might lament the fact that they
have to sit and sweat all their lives in parterres, and sit
and sweat in the world itself, merely because they cannot
manage to repress in themselves the fatal habit of im-
agining.

It is to Prokofieff's honor that he recognized the beauty
of the aid proffered him by the old Venetian playwright.
If "L'Amore delle Tre Melerancie," as it issues from his
hands, gives few indications that he is musically creative,
it nevertheless offers in innumerable spots signs that a
very alert wit has been at work. As a librettist, as a
deviser of amusing spectacles, the young Russ is admirable. The acted and spoken portions of "L'Amour

des Trois Oranges" were delightful, for the reason that, in composing his libretto, he had given a new life to the very informing spirit of Gozzi's plays. Certainly, Prokofieff was far more faithful to Count Carlo's dry and mischievous genius than the program's statement "The Love of Three Oranges. Words and music by Serge Prokofieff. Suggested by Carlo Gozzi" might have led one to believe. He did not, to begin with, make the error committed by Schiller when he adapted another of Gozzi's comedies, "Turandot" to the needs of the German stage. He did not seek to breathe human souls into the characters. He left them what they originally were, marionettes with the organs of men, automatic playing-cards which the stage-magician Tchelio and the Christmas-pantomime witch Fata Morgana might play out against each other as gamesters trump down ten-spots and jacks. The prince remains, what he was in Gozzi's version, a splenetic infant.

Indeed, as it stands, the libretto is a most ingenious and honorable piece of reconstruction. The scenes which have been eliminated are of the sort of explanatory incisions, conversations between villains, which were necessary to the languorously conducted stage in the eighteenth century, but which modern tempi of performances have rendered useless. Condensations have been happily effected throughout. To the scene of the tournament, where the hypochondriac prince for the first time laughs, and in so doing draws upon himself the curse of Fata Morgana which compels him to attain the love of an orange, there has been added one of the subsequent scenes, much to the improvement of both. Well done, too, is the scene of the encounter with the terrible and amorous cook in the castle of the guardian of the enchanted fruit. Prokofieff seems to have gathered intimations from the

scenario and Gozzi's own account of the memorable
first performance of the comedy, and then re-felt the
business in true comic vein.

In particular, the rôle assigned to the "absurdities"
carries out perfectly the Venetian's intentions. The composer has kept these curious creatures on the stage
throughout the entire action. He has placed them in two
little towers in the proscenium, from whence they spy upon
the scene, make ironic comments, mock the boasts of the
magician, and, occasionally, invade the boards for the purpose of changing the course of the action when it becomes
intolerable to them. For example, when the third princess
delivered from the orange-skin threatens to follow her two
predecessors and perish of thirst, the "absurdities," unable
longer to bear with the massacre, project "love" into
the universe. One of their number is sent onto the stage
with a bucket of water, which the prince finds, and holds
to the parching mouth. And then the princess, having
drunk, turns to the prince and says, "Tu m'as sauvé la
vie"; and he, like every gallant man who is informed by
a beautiful lady that he has given her life, modestly ac-
cepts the thanks, and adds, "Rein ne pouvait m'arrêter."

To be sure, the model has been unintelligently followed in several places, and local hits unintelligible to the
modern audience been preserved along with universal
applicabilities. In the second scene, Prokofieff lets
Trouffaldino, examining carefully the expectorations of
the prince, exclaim

> Ce sont des rimes puantes!
> J'ai de suite reconnu l'odeur.

while the "absurdities," from their vantage-towers enlarge

Mais parbleu! Il le nourrit de vers martéliens,
Léandre, canaille!

Now it is not to be expected of modern audiences no
more in Russia than in France or America, that they shall
have read either Gozzi's memoirs, Symonds' excellent
study of their author, or possess the sufficiency of
knowledge of the history of Italian literature that ought
to be every college passman's, to comprehend why Leander Knave of Clubs should in his villainy have fed the
prince martellian verses, and why these, to the conviction
of all, would have polluted his entrails. Unless capacity
exists for recollecting the war of the aristocratic Granal-
leschi academy, of which Gozzi was a member, upon the
plebeian tragedies of the Abbé Chiari which were written
in lumbering martellian verse, the joke is lost. Tchelio
for us is not a slap at Goldoni, as he was for the Venetian
public of the mid-eighteenth century; nor Fata, the pro-
tectress of the wicked Leander, a caricature of Chiari's
muse. The allusions are as alien to us as are the costumes
of Longhi, and something modern ought to have been
found as substitute for this stale canal-water. One doubts
whether Prokofieff was aware of the significance of the
quip, and whether he did not accept it rather naïvely.
Certainly, had he comprehended it, he must have made
haste to bring it to date.

Still, there is so much life in Prokofieff's libretto that,
could it have stood alone, it must have been a delight.
Unfortunately, Gozzi cannot stand alone unaided to-day
upon the boards. His works remain scenarios; even the
later ones, in which, instead of leaving all of the dialogue
to the improvisation of his actors, he wrote down the
important speeches. They were in truth the libretti, the
accompaniments, to what Marsden Hartley would call

the "muscular music" of Sacchi's troupe. The improvisation, the gestures, the movements, the *lazzi*, of this perhaps most accomplished band produced by the *commedia dell' arte*, festooned the bare posts Count Carlo hewed. Some substitute for this irrevocable art has to be found by the modernizer. Schiller, for example, found it in the great-hearted flood of his own poetry. Volmoeller, a more recent adapter, tried to find it in verse plus Reinhardt's staging plus Busoni's incidental music. Prokofieff turned to the machinery of grand opera, to the orchestra and the singing actors. But he turned pretty much in vain. For his score does little to aid the comedy. It drags upon it rather, it is so savorless. Gozzi, Russian stage-decorators, comedians of the Chicago Opera Association: these were the performance the night in the Manhattan Opera House. The composer, scarce at all.

When Serge Prokofieff wrote his score, he did not create, as Gozzi created. He did not achieve a conception; did not write a music that had beneath it a single feeling, and was fresh in style and sharp of edge as all things born of real feeling are. Between "L'Amour des trois Oranges" and to select a recent and successful example of opéra-bouffe, "L'Heure Espagnole," there lies a gulf; for the reason that Ravel had an idea of his own, and made therewith a musical shape which intensifies tenfold the stage-business, whereas Prokofieff seems to have had not an idea but a sort of wish. He has not recreated Gozzi, for his music is of very little interest. Rather, he seems to have come to Gozzi in the hope of being released into creativity by him. So his music falls to tLe level of the illustration of a text. It is made up of small and not very thrilling bits. To be sure, the score is not entirely flat. A certain modicum of wit cannot be denied it. There are a number of happy bits of stylistic and instrumental

burlesque in it that make one laugh. Particularly amusing are the occasional parodies of Debussy. The stupid
King of Clubs, embodiment of the gloom which sicklies
o'er grand opera, sings most often in the ancestral tone
which recalls, impishly, Aërkel. It was certainly a genial
moment which decided the composer to make the en-
amoured cook in Greonte's castle sing in the accent of
a Massenet heroine. The parodies of operatic ensembles
at the end of the first and the last acts are good clowning.
There are even some moments which interest musically.
The duo of the lovers in the desert scene is pretty. The
music played while the princess waits for the return of
her affianced, and the scenery is transformed, has atmosphere. There is design in the *lamentoso sostenuto* of the
prince.

Moreover, the intentions of the composer, manifest in
the work, are worthy of study. Significant is the fact
that he has suppressed all picturesque detail from his
music, left all scene-painting in the impressionist sense out
of it. His ideal seems to have been musical comedy of
the sort "Don Giovanni" is. Arresting, too, is the fact
that he seems to have sought to compose with the naïveté
of a child; strumming out his little marches, intermezzi
and other of the more set pieces, with the nonchalance
of an improviser. But little came of these intentions.
The music, like all other of Prokofieff's efforts in sustained
composition, is dull. It lacks personal edge, and it is
monotonous. He has not yet learned to instrumentate
with distinction, and passages where his orchestra re-
minds one a little of the accompaniments to the Chopin
concerti, still occur. Too often, his wit is limited to the
production of flatus-like sounds from the bassoons and
brass. It was rather meager cleverness which was contented to use the noise of a hickaphone to accompany the

flight of the prince and Trouffaldino through the air. Prokofieff may have decided upon writing with the nonchalance of a child. But he shows none of the child's wonder, or the child's freedom of rhythmical invention. As usual, his work is rhythmically poor. The march is brayingly empty. If the intermezzo, in its hurry, catches for a moment the spirit of comedy, it loses it through its redundancy and lack of contrast. Perhaps Gozzi demands in his musicians a certain dryness; perhaps just such a dry recitative as Prokofieff has attempted to give his singers. The old Ventian was sere of heart, certainly. But Prokofieff has caught nothing of any intrinsic charm.

Something which happened to Gozzi has not happened to Prokofieff: for this reason his opéra-bouffe remains a pedestal without a statue. Both men; and the young Tieck, and all other romantic ironists as well, have faced, every one in his own age, an almost identical world. The Venetian, the romantic Germans, the young Russian, all of them have belonged to a society which was being discarded by life. Gozzi belonged to the aristocracy of a decaying state. Tieck and Brentano were men who lived in the shadow of the middle ages midmost a Europe which was being plowed open by the French Revolution. Prokofieff belongs to the unrooted fashionable Russia which has gone finally to a fall. All have been partisans of causes in which they have had no faith. All have been left dry by life, and felt with some bitterness their dryness, and seen the world an empty nurse's tale, a ridiculous self-deception of the dreaming ego. But in Gozzi, and in Tieck, some secret intensity, some capacity for passion, met the incrushing world, made of the melancholy discovery an experience, and helped them at least to laugh in the face of the emptiness. For one moment, at least, these men must have escaped from their subjectivity, and seen it impersonally. And in that moment of release they must have conceived, and been enabled to snatch a pleasure out of the void, and sculpt their nothing into solid form. It is this experience, it seems, which Proko-fieff has never had. His own state, his own incapacity to have any experience outside music, may have made him bitter and mordant; the freshness which the others had has not appeared in him. It is not there when he is serious, in his piano-concerti. It is not there when he is merry. Had Georges Auric, or any other member of the Group of Six, with whom Prokofieff has certain affinities of spirit, set the play of Gozzi, the score might have been brutal; but it would have had teeth. But Prokofieff wants the life of even these gamins. And until he achieves some vibrancy of his own, his music will continue to bore us.

March, 1922.

The Tragedy of Gustav Mahler

SOMEWHAT as Dante and his guide stood before certain damned in Hell do we stand before the failed endeavors of Gustav Mahler. We cannot pass these hulking haggard symphonies and songs as we pass by other failures offered us by the concert seasons. Stale and tired and scarce living as these musics are, they nevertheless, each time we encounter any one of them, make us to stop still in pity and turn distressedly about them. For they are monuments of anguished aborted life, like indeed to torture-masses devised by the imagination of a ferocious medieval god for the punishment of transgressors against him. They call before the vision the blocks of ice in the circle of traitors in the Inferno that contain each its wretched congealed soul. They, too, these dusty and feeble instrumental piles, are in some strange terrible way part living. Underneath the heaped banalities, beneath false Beethoven and conscious naïvetés and unfresh lyricism, there writhes a vein of living green, and struggles piteously for release. We sense a caked and buried face; hear parched lips and cracked laryngeal chords straining to frame speech. The hoarse and infinitely fatigued voice is seeking to sob, to pray, to bless, but its tone breaks and rasps and faints in the dust. It seems to be begging something of us, entreating us to do something. But what it is it demands of us we do not know, or, if we guess, do not know at all how to meet and gratify it.

The fact that the composer of Mahler's nine symphonies

238

and many songs was a Prospero among conductors, a profound and magical interpreter of Beethoven and of Wagner, a poet who made other orchestral leaders seem pedestrian, is not what makes his efforts at creation appear torture-blocks in our eyes. It is not pity that stirs us. We are neither stirred nor wrung by the scores of Weingartner, also a great conductor and an unsuccessful composer. What hurts us when Mahler's works are performed is, that his miscarriages refer always to a living impulse behind them, to an inventive power not unrelated to his interpretative; that each gargantuan symphony and song-cycle bears evidence to the failure of a creative surge to realize itself in any solid form. Something did go down in battle in Mahler's compositions that was noble and high, and that we would gladly have seen triumphant. Even in the pompous kapellmeistermusik of his fifth, sixth, and seventh symphonies, sharp vestiges of originality pierce through the billowing rubble. Sometimes, it is nothing more than his miraculous gift of instrumentation that is green among the charred ruins; and all that reconciles us in all the world to the man, are some moments when the music permits us to observe his usage of the modern orchestra, so much more simple and reserved and sharp than Strauss'; grants us the pleasure of hearing the cutting razor edge of a band in which brass and reeds predominate, of feeling the nasal, astringent, brilliant quality of his favorite daring combinations of wood and trumps.

Sometimes, to this salvaged joy another adds itself. Mahler manages at times, despite second-handedness, suspiciousness of thematic material, to establish well a definite mood. Even if we blush a little at his themes, we feel, say, the excitement of the nightly, death-haunted bacchanal, in the first section of "Das Lied von der

Erde." At intervals, the atmosphere of a landscape is fixed; the world darkens visibly as a solitary oboe executes its repeated quaver; and for a brief while, we taste something of the food the composer intended setting before us, know his sick yearning for life, his loneliness, the bitter savor of ashes on his lips as he waits along for death. Or, a shimmer of the living world is caught in a splinter of mirror, and we feel in Mahler's music the nerve-weariness of men in our time, or get a naturalistic picture of shrilling work-people on holiday parade to the parks, or whiff old-world whole-heartedness while a horn sings as sings the posthorn in German forests. Or, a passage of sustained music suddenly makes its appearance; the interlude of the last section of "Das Lied von der Erde," with its harshly croaking clarinets and horns, its groaning, mordant polyphony; or one of the gallows-humorous scherzi, half scurrilous, half fantastic, so original with Mahler. And for an instant we are half-reconciled with the legend that the man was a great composer.

But the living stuff is lost in the great unfilled voids of the canvases. A small power is wrecked in the attempt to develop a space entirely too great for the reach of the undertaker. As forms, things, these symphonies crumble and do not live. The living breath does not run through the instrumental masses and make them with each tone they give, sculpt some great reality that was in the heart of the composer, and that he had to discover to the world. The great embracing feeling that descended from the head of a Beethoven or a Wagner into their fingertips and through these into the cohorts of instruments, we know, did not succeed in leaving Mahler's cranium. We guess his intentions from his programs and his reported conversations. We guess them from certain associations revealed by the themes and instruments themselves.

But while there is always in Mahler something present for the eye; there is most often nothing for the ear. His works are like vast spineless ships that look majestical enough while they lie high on the beach, but that break in two or capsize or sink as soon as one attempts to float them on the sea. Mahler is helpless on nearly every page. With all his prodigious orchestral technique he cannot touch. There is always the beginning of something in his scores. His vast and Bruckner-like themes heave on with terrific stride, then break down suddenly, and there is a void, while the band makes certain developments or roundings-out that have no existence for the sense. A song begins; a few notes are sweet, then, suddenly, there is a banal, stale note, from which one turns as from a sour breath. Such are the turns in the "Chorus Mysticus" of the Eighth Symphony, on the words "Das unbeschreibliche, hier wird es getan"; in the twelfth and thirteenth bars of the last movement of the Third, where Mahler attempts to round out his pseudo-Beethovenish adagio theme; in the second section of "Das Lied von der Erde," where the singer gives "Ich hab' Erquickung Not"; in innumerable other spots of the score.

Or, he begins a broad flowing movement as in the finale of the Third Symphony, and loses momentum. He begins endless recapitulations. He repeats over and over again sweet cadences or harmonies on which he has happened; lingers over them, fond and narcissistic as a mother over the antics of a spoiled child. When he has to conclude, under pain of becoming a bore even to his own patient self, his ending is quite arbitrary, a suddenly stitched-on close, with much brilliant brass and percussion. And, so, the positive achievements of his talent are counterbalanced and made naught overwhelmingly by his banalities. The gallows-humorous scherzi are followed

by the sort of trumpet-tunes which are very nice for the
servant girl when she goes out Sunday afternoons. A
fine bit of scene-painting, a passage of poignant music
right off the wheel of modern life, is suddenly dragged
down by a "consoling" theme of organ-grinder beauty.
Whole movements palpably "faked," written without sincere feeling, as the third, fourth and fifth of "Das Lied,"
spoil what pleasure one can extract from those sincerely
felt. And even where there is some success in representation, the testimony of haggard senses and tired pulses
which exists in everything Mahler brought forth, leaves
one with a painful sense of failed life. Not even the
energy and affection lavished by Conductor Mengelberg
on every one of Mahler's scores he essays; nor even the
unflagging effort to relieve the intention and make the
hollow music communicate what Mahler wanted to say,
can lift these sinking bulks.

It went to parch in the wilderness, Mahler's vine of
life, because, whether or not he was aware fully of his
motive, his work was built about his own person. Mahler's center was not in his composition, much as he
thought it there. It remained always within himself;
and although a vivid impulse drove him to selfless expression, a far stronger wrenched the impulse into service
to an arid egoism. The man was slave, more than ever
he guessed, to a desire of setting his own figure amid the
symbols and panoply of greatness. He needed the public
to feel certain glorious things about him, untoward him;
to take him and place him by its reverence and love and
admiration among the immortals, among the serene figures
grouped in the Walhalla of musicians about Beethoven.
It was, in spite of his belief, Beethoven that he wanted
to be more than Gustav Mahler; for he needed bitterly
that the public perceive in him the benign symphonist,

the great heart-whole lover of men; he wanted the love of
men to come out to him, he wanted to give them something that would force from them toward himself a glow-
ing stream of affection. And this motive was always
uppermost in his breast when he approached his worktable.

For Mahler was, there cannot be question, one of those
unfortunate persons who cannot center their interest in
another human breast, and give themselves completely in
love. He was, certainly, one of those unfortunates for
whom life inevitably must represent a struggle toward
an ambitiously conceived goal, must have a definite ego-
centric purpose: because the living of life itself is so
devoid of deep satisfactoriness to them. It was easy
enough for Goethe to declare, "Es kommt offenbar im
Leben aufs Leben, und nicht auf ein Resultat desselben
an." For things in themselves were nourishing to him.
But for poor Gustav Mahler, life was a waste, a proces-
sion of disappointments, a garden whose smoldering
fruits turned ashen in his mouth. Precisely what it was
that kept him from properly slaking his thirst at the
brook that runs right through the front dooryard of all
the world, we cannot more than guess about. The man's
confession that of the impressions which he tried to
realize in his music the greater portion was received
during the first five years of his existence, turns one's
guesses in the direction of a hurt done him in infancy.

It is not to be entertained, that he, any more than any
other normally intelligent child, entered the world in-
capacitated to fulfill himself toward his fellows. His
yearning, so perpetually green in him, for the days when
he was a nursling on the Bohemian plain; the hearkening
back to the impressions of infancy that might have come
to the bright little boy of the poor tavern-keepers; his

visions of death, all his hours, as a return homeward, an
entrance into the secret inner life of the universe, are not,
we suspect, merely the fantastic thinking of a man who,
having never possessed a capacity for living, consoles
himself by glorifying the state closest to pre-natal existence. In their sincerity, their earnestness, they seem
rather more indications of the fact that the bliss of this
time had been so very intense, so inordinately sensitizing
that the attachment to his own infantile nature became
overstrong in the man; that it displaced zest for adventure, and made the pain of maturity too unbearable for
hearty acceptation. It seems strange to consider that the
man whom one knew as a harried, bitterly compressed-
mouthed conductor, a tortured head cut loose from the
body, should once have been an infant clutched too hard
to the breast of a woman. But such we are forced to see
him; it is only in this fashion that we are able to explain
his crippledness. All children meet the world, death, and
the devil as they grow. Only, in certain, some inherent,
unbroken toughness which nature gave them at birth
asserts itself, and closes the wounds inflicted by the
grisly companions. But in Mahler, the ability to find
the way to men had been enfeebled by oversensitization;
and the wounds inflicted on him became fatal.

And it would, indeed, have required, that he might
meet and repel the enemies in wait for him, an almost
inordinately stalky toughness in the inner column of
young Mahler's spirit. For Mahler was born a Jew.
And to be born a Jew, particularly in the Austria of the
1860's, was not intensely conducive to the sustainment of
that fresh faith in life, that relaxed love of men, from
which great song springs. It was, on the contrary, a cir-
cumstance full of baleful encouragement to those who
had been hurt, to button tighter and hug ever closer to

themselves the ancient gray overcoat of fear. The quick
was menaced by the sharp swords of the repressed but
very living hostility of the surrounding population; and
to expose it was to invite almost inevitable pain; to have
more rocks thrown on the wavering column of confidence
in self, satisfaction in self, faith in the greenness of life;
to have ever heavier chains hung on the arms when they
moved of instinct in the great embracing rhythms. For
whatever in the growing lad wanted cause for not pro-
jecting his interest, his love into the objective world, and
fulfilling himself, there waited (as it waits in every land
on every child of Jews) the distrust, the antagonism, the
exclusiveness, of alien peoples, with its gift of the sentiment of inner unworth, of tribal inferiority. And this
fact must have helped arrest the already inhibited spon-
taneity of the heart, with unresting counsel of niggard-
liness.

And then, the atmosphere of the Jewish community
itself does not make free, healthy living, easy. Generation had bequeathed to generation, in a sort of convulsive
laying on of hands, a nervous tension, a sort of clamp
and suspension, in the entrails, a strain all over the body,
legacy of centuries of uncertain, difficult existence. Even
in the Austria of the 60's, as in the America of the new
century, where fear of physical persecution does not always press, the necessities of life still forced and do force
a sort of unhealthful wakefulness in the Jew, a fear of
the sense, a distrust of relaxation, a lurid sort of consciousness. The Germans and Czechs about Mahler's
home, for example, could let go their wakefulness; could
let themselves down into the landscape as cattle let themselves down upon the sward to munch. They, the farm-
people, could accept the moment, drain it fearlessly and
irresponsibly as they drained their steins. Mahler, the

unrooted, the inheritor of trading-wits, could never do so.

Besides, the world into which Mahler issued in career, had little power to make good the wrong. The sudden industrialization of Germany and of Austria, the strongly "Americanizing" tendency of society, had taken the accent from the quality of things and placed them on the quantity of them. The artist has to do with the preservation of the quality of life; and the artist was not invited by a time that had no spiritual values. Or, if he was, he was invited only to stimulate nerves wearied by a harried, empty existence, to give sensations to folk incapable of procuring them for themselves. Had Mahler been strong, it is possible he might have resisted the world, as other men have done. But he was weak, and so he could not help being weakened further by the vulgar atmosphere in which he had to share. Publicity was the mother of the Muses. All the world was a stage; never might one forget the presence of an audience. All about him was a frenzied Bismarkianization of music; a St. Vitus dance of concerts, operas, festivals, premières, nether-Rhenish music-debauches, Napoleonic careers modeled on misconceptions of the life of Wagner and of Nietzsche, newspaper-log-rolling by music-publishers, Richard Strauss, a great externalized music life. Poison must have come into the man with every breath, much as he would have avoided it.

And thus the writing of "great" music became the end of Mahler's days. Since he had not within him the power to satisfy himself in living; since he could never quite be a man in the street; he turned to composition, turned to it more and more to indemnify himself as he aged. Since he had the rudiments of creativity in him, and could feel the immensity of the emotional release which Beethoven and which Wagner had gotten from their art; since he himself got an enormous release in presenting their works; he commenced, with logical illogicality, aping the external attributes of their art in hopes of gaining the power of self-expression that had been theirs. He set out to become "great." For being sterile, he supposed that their ability to love, to create, had come to them through a power over musical means; and supposed that if he made the gesture of grandeur, and if the public responded to that gesture as it responded to the music of the masters, he would achieve what a kinder nature had given them and not given him. So he took his talent, and began forcing it to flesh arbitrarily conceived schemes. Perceiving the philosophical weight of Beethoven and Wagner, he began searching for an aprioristic metaphysical orientation. It was a literary composer, in the bad sense, that he became. His ideas were not permitted to come to him as musical shapes and lines. It was rather more as autobiographical material, as philosophic theory, as haunting and vaguely outlined emotion, that work seems first to have entered his consciousness. The process of music-making seems to have been a secondary one; a turning of concepts *into* music with the assistance of a prodigious musical technique and a virtuosic orchestral sense. That, the strange unfreshness of his idiom demonstrates. Beethoven, Schubert, Mendelssohn, Wagner, Bruckner, Brahms, haunt his pages. For, feeling nothing so much as the desire to feel, to be creative, to be musicful; he perforce thought the thoughts that had already come into the world. He was the sentimentalist, searching out emotion for its own sake, and luxuriating in it. And one feels always that, whenever he did manage to achieve emotions, he never let them do anything to him, really; and that there was something unhealthily wakeful in him watching himself under the influence of feel-

ing; prodding him on to register an idea which might be
of use to him in composition; pouncing on him at every
quiver of his nerves with the cry, "Now, at last, you are
giving me something which I can use in creating!"
Never does he seem entirely lost. Even his naïveté, his
Glockenbimbamblümchen vein, wants a complete ingenu-
ousness. The childlike tones are hollow; there is something haggard and worn in the pretended overflow of
spirits. He is putting on clothes, we see; he is trying to
feel so that something will happen to him and make him
like the strapping and heart-fresh and solid Germans who
made the style of the folk-songs.

He had all the non-artist's obsession with technical
processes. His scores seem written with a view to the
work of the pedantic analyzer; he was asking the pedants
to crown him magister. His symphonies are stiff-jointed
with a sort of formal classicism. They have not so much
the spirit as the mannerism of the great classic form-
givers. On the engraved page, the writing looks like
Haydn's, like Beethoven's. But it wants indeed the
necessity, the athleticism, of theirs. And, since he could
not feel, he took to making music by brute force; drove
his orchestra to climaxes with sadistic vehemence, as
though he would ravish an esthetic emotion from the
hearers. He called for immense apparatus, reaching a
ridiculous apotheosis in the "Symphonie der Tausend" in
the effort to achieve greatness through enormity of means.
He dragged by the hair into his works poems of Goethe
and Nietzsche, of Klopstock and Rhabanus Maurus, as
well as lyrics from "Des Knaben Wunderhorn," in the
hope of making these giants labor for him. One of his
commentators marvels at the daring with which Mahler,
in his Third Symphony, goes from a setting of Nietzsche's
"Drunken Song" to a setting of a folk-lyric. Sancta

Simplicitas!   Poor Mahler would have gone from a setting of St. Francis' "Hymn to the Sun" to a setting of the
Pennsylvania time-table, had he thought the deed enormous and revolutionary and creative.   He would have
written a solo for the Saint Esprit, had he thought it
possible to persuade that potentate to participate in the
performance of one of his symphonies.   His was indeed a
piling of many suffering Pelions on many indignant
Ossas.

And still, we cannot dismiss the man with a wave of
the hand.   Sentimentalist though he was, there was too
much intensity, too much heartfelt yearning in him to
make his case a ludicrous one.   There is something not
unnoble in the longing for the power to know the human
lot, when it is passionately felt.   And Mahler's cry for
life was the cry of a great ruptured heart for health.
There are too many genial moments in his compositions;
there is too much marvelously piercing color in his instrumentation, to let us forget how great a potentionality
lay in him awaiting redemption.   It is with a profound
sympathy that we watch this poor sick Jew, years since
his decease, still wring his hands in the sere mounds of his
music, and call to the universe to give unto him a thing
which the universe cannot give, and that is found either
in the human heart itself, or nowhere at all.

March, 1922.

expense of the deserved sleep of the Mendelssohn Reformation Symphony and its unhappy kin? No, it was to the Tomb that they addressed themselves for material. That had to give up its contents for appreciation. Kadaververwerthung.

Symptoms of the malady have been shown by the Society since ever Mr. Bodansky became its Patiomkin. The scholarly man has bettered the presentations of the music, which were not too smooth before he assumed Prime Ministership. His feeling for style is almost perfect. But, due to his unfortunate gusto for the feebler and prettier works of the German romantics, he has been diluting programs which since the foundation of the organization were never very strong or very decided. At least, before his consulship, nobody got up and sang "Infelice." But since its commencement, they have sung "Infelice" and unhappier yet; the orchestra has played other stirring things by Mendelssohn—"Son and Stranger," for example; and a chorus with four soloists and an orchestra gave a performance of a cantata by Schumann entitled "Der Rosenpilgerfahrt," which the unhappy Robert must have written during the first stages of paresis, just before he tried to drown himself in the Rhine. There were also repeated performances of not very necessary things by Brahms for horn and women's voices, and a Jessonda or two. (A Jessonda appears to be a musical form in which you anticipate every note three bars before it arrives, and when it arrives it sounds just as tame as you imagined.) But, even last season the Society of the Friends of Music retained some of the livelier color it had once shown, or given earnest of eventually showing. The organization which one would have wanted it to be, the organization which one wants for New York so that there shall be some vital progressive musical life in this great oafish capital, it never was, it need scarce be remarked. We want in New York a band of friends to music who are at the forefront of musical culture; who will bring it about that the veritably new music which is being produced in the world as well as the unknown classics shall be made known to the New York that needs to know it; and who so heartily believe in their work that they will see that many performances and not only one, are held, and that unfamiliar work is spoon-fed to the recalcitrant public as Wagner once was fed to it. Something of the nature will have to appear if musical New York is ever to cease being ten years behind Paris and five behind London. This responsibility the Society of the Friends of Music had always rather timidly evaded. Certain very important services it has, indeed, rendered the art of music; its discovery to America of the music of Ernest Bloch alone puts us everlastingly in its debt. Other rare events, too, have taken place through it; one was given to hear the "Kammersinfonie" of Schoenberg; one heard ultramodern recitals by Arthur Rubinstein and recitals of pre-Bachian piano-music by Harold Bauer; the Philadelphia Orchestra found its way through the society into New York. But single performances of new and strange work seemed to satisfy the organization's conscience. And the research into the whole field of music; the presentation of Monteverdi and Purcell and Rameau, of Scriabine and Strawinsky and the later more acid Schoenberg, and Bartók and Satie and Ornstein; that, one bitterly missed, and cursed the timidity or the stupidity that let it go unmade.

This season, when any association of friends of music should have seen to it that works like "Lieder des Pierrot lunaire," "L'histoire du soldat," "Socrate," and the last sonatas of Scriabine, and Berg and Bartók and Auric were wishes to conduct orchestral concerts, its concerts have become almost entirely orchestral. Now, were Mr. Bodansky the type of creative, enthusiastic musician, things might be well with it still. Unfortunately, he has not the poet's swift, sensitive life. No doubt, he is a genuine addition to the musical situation in the city. He is a solid scholar, and represents a sort of rock of honest musicianship among his more flashy and worthless *confrères*. A person to respect, distinctly! But he has always been more of a cerebral than a temperamental. There is a schoolmaster in him. And, of late, his rather morose intellectualism seems to have grown. New York, the miserable, has unfortunately tended to dry him as it has dried so many others. He has gotten, a little, to resemble in his person an abstraction by Picasso. Have you not noticed it? There are moments when he seems to have been taken into the mind and issued reorganized *more geometrico*. There is something about his long black frock-coat that resembles a concept. The back of his head is pure idea; and the relationship between head and square narrow shoulders seems, once in a while, a smart bit of Hegelian dialectic. Many opposites coincide in him. Now, it is well known that the more purely mental we become, the more stagnant our senses. Sentimentality oftentimes accompanies the most rigorous scholastic intellectuality. In Mr. Bodansky, as he himself threatens to rise more and more completely into the mind, the affection for the coventionally pretty classics is developing to monstrous size. And, having found a society which is only too happy to give him every opportunity he craves, he has inundated us with floods of sugary music, and given promise of a most cadaverous future for the society of his "Friends."

April, 1922.

All-American Night

It is to be hoped that one of the stout young Frenchmen who appear every week or two in the port of New York and evince an interest in the symptoms of a native American art second in vibrancy only to their interest in the American well-to-do, was present at the concert given April 29th by the Music Guild. Was such a double-breast-coated one in the MacDowell Gallery that evening, it is certain that a single visitor has had his curiosity about American musical production, at least, satisfied, and yet been properly informed of the quality of the expression. A single visitor, will, at the conclusion of his few months' trip, board La France and sail Parisward and still be unprepared to tell his war-enfeebled home intellects that the blues and jazz are the United States music. It was, indeed, a rarely compact and truthful picture of American musical production at the moment when its grand general uselessness is commencing to shrink before sudden unexpected flashes and rumblings of latent power, that was offered its public by the Guild. Past and future of native composition, the great, dreary, empty past and the young, uncertain, fitful future, showed themselves beautifully proportionately. The promise of coming years was in the grouping of the nine musicians who constitute the American Music Guild: for the first time, it seems, in our story, the younger men are commencing to work together; individualities are beginning to discover means of nourishing themselves. But if the future shone in the fact of this new alliance grown out sort given out by men who have very little contact with anything in the world save music, and who are entirely unaware of the fact. The composers are, there is no doubt, the most admirable of men. New York cannot afford to lose many minutes of either Walter Kramer's or Deems Taylor's time. But they are not, when they compose, moving with what is moving in life. They are fugitive from their own personalities. The world in which they breathe does not seep into their composition, and color it. Like the audience's, their life remains somewhere within them, and never touches the earth.

At the base of the program, just above the tail-legend STEINWAY PIANO USED, there ran the line Trio in one Movement Op. 7—Harold Morris. This notice should have shed some cheer over the evening. For the afternoon at Æolian Hall last year when Harold Morris, with the assistance of his friend, Albert Stoessel, performed three of his own sonatas, had given one another excuse for believing that things were about to move in the musical field this side the billows. The two piano sonatas and the one sonata for violin and piano of the young Texan had shown themselves much of the rather loose, floppy, undistinguished sort of music which we are accustomed to receive at the hands of our musicians; but certain movements, certain passages, had arrested one, and won respect and even wonder. It was noticeable that the central slow movements, passive and quiet, had greater plasticity and originality than the outer. It was, in them, as though gases had suddenly condensed and formed a solid. The idiom was not personal, to be sure; the sorcerer was still very much the apprentice; but a black piano chord, a theme, did something. Here was American music one wanted to grow to know, not leave and never sight again.

Nevertheless, the evening at the MacDowell Gallery, while the concert was plodding along, one could not help being a little apprehensive. It was, after all, quite possible that the impression gained last year had been rosied o'er by some extraneous oversanguine temper. There was enough in the works that were occupying this late April evening to make one very tender of believing any movement in progress in musical affairs on this Atlantic shore. Scarce, however, had Messrs. Morris, Stoessel, and Lucien Schmitt attacked on piano, violin, and 'cello the trio, than one knew no extraneous mood had deceived. The blood jetted smoothly. One had something to nourish one. Here, at last, was some one who began to have the weight of a composer. The three years that had elapsed between the composition of the youngest of his three sonatas, performed last season, and the trio, had taken none of the sincerity and push from Harold Morris and had augmented the power considerably. The excitability was greater; the music denser. The ideas gushed forth in fine abundance. The sentimental element, the element which in every young American ought to be called the MacDowellesque, had been warred on. A sort of savage rhythmical impulse, and a color influenced by negro spirituals, but not intellectualized as it sometimes is in the work of John Powell, had put in appearance. Something flat and not quite fine there was in the music, still. There were many moments when the composer relapsed into the manner hereditary to the American composer, and proclaimed the obvious. One does not recall with pleasure the peroration of the trio, with its "steigerung" and grandiose finish. Besides, the music seemed a trifle chaotic. It seems possible that the composer's best ideas come to him while he is in the heated process of composition. Not all the four themes which support the work are equally racy and interesting. His strong moments seemed always a little improvisational, as though they had appeared under his pen suddenly he knew not from where, and made him wonder a little whether he was not a trifle mad. Morris has some sort of lurking savage down in the sub-cellar of his being, a wild man, part Yank, part nigger, part something else. On top the cellar door there sit sisters and cousins and aunts who do not like the wild man anywhere but in sub-cellars. But he is commencing to break through with his complicated rhythms and his savage excitability.

And out into the city night in Fifty-fifth Street one rushed, sure that a new situation was reached in American music. For Harold Morris is not a solitary swallow. There are others of the same feather and flock. One is here, one there, several in this place; there is one youth from the Trenton suburbs who seems one of the most musically talented creatures this country has produced. Scarcely a one has developed a characteristically personal idiom as yet. But there are several who are using a derivative idiom in the fashion in which men who have developed their individualities have used, apparently, in the time of their minority, material of the type already pretty well developed by their immediate elders. One writes with a Strawinsky-like acidity. Another has been impressed by the formal experiments of Satie. But both have something of individuality to express, and the personal in them struggles with the reflected. It is, then, no longer true, go, Stranger, to Sparta tell, that there is no vitality in the native musical production. What has been characteristic of the painting and the writing of the land has now become characteristic of the music. The country can produce really gifted youth. Society has become sufficiently settled to permit the talent to assert itself; there is even, in this timorous herd, enough of a real community to permit the musical gesture, the gesture of the interpenetrated group, to be made.

What remains undecided, what constitutes to-day the problem of the American musician, is whether this impulse is sufficiently strong to send the composer through his education in taste, his passion unbroken. It has not yet been proven, that our young musicians are sufficiently strong to go to the past, to go to the European experimenters, as they must in order to develop their intellectual comprehension of their art, and still continue to express themselves freshly. It has been Morris', as instance, good fortune that he has expressed uninhibitedly his banal and unrefined facets together with his richer, truer; for the latter could not have appeared without the former. To inhibit one were to inhibit both. But in order that he may grow, it is necessary that he develop his critical powers, his sense of beautiful form, either through study with a good magister or, if he can, on his own; and it is highly speculative whether such a course might not lead to a damming of the impulse. Esthetic development has been the rock on which many a good American talent has foundered. It is there, surely, that poor Charles Griffes met ship-wreck. And yet, it is for the Brahmsian assimilation of musical culture; for the talent that can grow in intellectual mastery and still utter itself in freshness, that we wait. Such an one alone can give us the music that will make us, the herd, men indeed.

May, 1922.

The Bethlehem Festival

ALL summer long, the Bach Festival at Bethlehem has had me under its broad pinion. In the sky it has spread its delicate protective sail; if the season has seemed less long and less crude than it has been so many other years, it is not a little because of the high experience had in May. It was a double source of joy those cool green days in the little Pennsylvanian hill-city unsealed. I heard glorious music roundly presented; I found this purest beauty rearing itself like a Gothic dome in a sad American town; and the knowledge that for the hour in American land there has established itself a yearly music festival as noble in plan and in execution as was the Salzburg Mozart festival in the years before the war, has hovered like a benediction in gray and oppressive weather. Formerly, I thought that there existed nowhere in the States a place to which folk fared pilgrim-wise for the purpose of assisting at reverent and accomplished presentations of the work of an almighty composer; a spot wherein an artist has been permitted to create for himself the air most necessary to the life of his thought, and wherein for a day or two performers and audience live as do the lilies of the field merely for the sake of lifting into fullest light an immortal thing. I knew by name the Bach Festival of the Bethlehem Choir. But memories of certain end-season orchestral debauches in mid-western cities, had foolishly deterred me from testing it. To assist at the temple-service of music; to see fall the fruity evening sun as it fell across the Mirabellengarten after Dr. Muck in the Mozarteum had sent into farthest space the fugal close of the "Jupiter" symphony; to feel the night as it lay grand and ruddy and prolonged over the Isar when the fire-music of "Die Walküre" had dwindled into opal mist, and the doors of the Prinz-Regententheater were flung open, one had, it seemed to me, to cross sea-water and forfeit the American fact, and to lose oneself in the alien circumstances of a foreign society.

So sadly ignorant I might a good many years longer have remained, had not last springtime a certain orient star led me and several equally unwise persons to Bethlehem, and there let us drink draughts of Bach no whit less full and lucid than those of Mozart and of Wagner once offered by Salzburg and Munich and Bayreuth. Indeed, it was from a larger cup one quaffed in the Pennsylvanian than in the German festival towns. For here it was Bach's gorgeous-sounding music that was performed. This year two supreme examples of the eternal good-man's many masterpieces were presented. On the two successive days of the festival the "St. Matthew Passion" and the b-minor Mass were attacked, and for all the weaknesses of portions of the medium, marvelously well realized. One was not generally oppressed by the divine tragedy as one was when the Oratorio Society of New York under the baton of a Damrosch proceeded through it. One was not permitted to become a little drowsy during certain movements of the stupendous vocal symphony as one was last winter when Mr. Schindler and the Schola essayed it. The two sounding worlds dug deeply in. Bach was enormous over one as a firmament; for the two gigantic works, emanating from about the same years of the cantor's life, are dissimilar in feeling, and well-nigh as opposed to each other as two

that makes one feel something almost more Canadian than American at certain turnings amid the smoky air of Bethlehem, the place does not depart essentially from the type of second-class city in the United States. If it has its mountainy walls, its pretty hillside campus, and its bits of blazer-color supplied by Lehigh students lounging feet up on the porches of fraternity houses, it has also its river-front grim with the brutal bulks and chimneys of mills, its trolley lines running past numberless blocks of genteel dreary houses of the last century into the more modern Arcadia of the *Ladies' Home Journal,* and its corner drug-stores in whose windows repose majestically enormous brass-crowned glass vases apparently filled with liquids of chemical violet and blue. It contains one plaster-fresh hotel wherein a senatorial colored head-waiter addresses guests Bossuet-like with "We beg you sincerely to bear with us" when the restaurant service breaks down beneath the matutinal demands of famished Bach enthusiasts, and it takes the eggs an hour and a quarter to fry. It contains also several smaller older hotels where leather arm-chairs and attendant cuspidors stand behind the long plate window giving on the thoroughfare, and where waitresses of virginal demeanor recruited from the ranks of the lower middle classes serve vegetables in birds' bath-tubs. Much of the character of what is outside the walls of the Packard Memorial Church is within it, too. The apse contains six painted windows which, while pretending to represent three Old Testamentary and three New Testamentary worthies, are really exquisitely expressive of the feeble and sour representations of the spiritual forces made by the latter generations who have inhabited the environs. One could easily perceive the sons in that picture of paternal authority. Moses and Elias, if these indeed are they, look exactly like doddering old fatherly gentlemen whom the young ambitious could perfectly afford to neglect; while King David smiting his harp looks like a sporty banker with whiskers, turned a bit esthetic; a sort of Victorian Anthology Stedman in oriental silks; and wears his light-colored biretta at a raffish angle. The New Testamentary personages, on the other hand, look like nobody at all.

No, it is an individual has made flourish this great grave beauty a few hundreds of yards away from the mills of the Bethlehem Steel Company! In a little nervy man, half schoolmasterish, half poetical; in two lengthy hands like violins that seem to reason and to coax music from out the throats of an hundred odd work-people of a Pennsylvania industrial town; in the spectacled face which registers every nuance of a most subtle and complex and severe art; in a small slender body suffused entirely with the excitement of Bach's music, there resides the lever which has brought Bach and Bethlehem together, and made a temple-service of musical art for the United States. It is said that twenty years ago Dr. Wolle went to Germany and heard Bach, and returned full of the will to organize the compositions of this composer into the life of his native city. And out of that feeling of a single individual for a work, a kunstkörper has grown. Support has been found in the pocket of a man who probably ignores nothing more than he does the spirit that expressed itself in a "Passion according to St. Matthew." A medium has been created out of folk who in their pristine state probably most heartily preferred the tunes of Harry von Tilzer to the chorales of the Leipzig cantor. Among the tenors and bassos who sat high up in the tribune in the Memorial Church, there were doubtless some of the selfsame valiant steel-puddlers who, it used to be rumored, hastily recruited, assured the strength of the Lehigh eleven in its yearly game against the team of Lafayette. One had feared the dragon of conventionality how many times behind faces little different from those of the serried rows of girls in white! And yet, what sincerity and intelligence in the voices of the huskies to whom small solo parts had been assigned! What veritably ecstatic poses of the head, what ecstatic suffusion of the neck-cords, among the women as the performance progressed! One saw bodies that had summoned themselves complete and gave themselves complete in the spirit of Bach into the long outstretched persuasive hands of the conductor crouched luminous and self-forgetful in his chair.

There was the intermission of an hour between the performance of the Gloria and the Credo the second day of the festival; and during that time I climbed up the green campus of the university and stood on the ivy-randed terrace of one of the buildings. From that parapet one sees far away over Bethlehem to the north. On the horizon, the gray sky of coldish May was slashed with lights of white and whitey-blue. Below, in the belfry of the Memorial Church, the brass choir was intoning, on solemn trombones and trumpets, chorales of Bach. As I stood gazing out over the fuming town towards the cloud-confines, there was in me the exaltation that comes whenever something perfect has taken place for me in American land. The light sang over the harsh scene as then it always sings. A beauty somewhat like that in certain of Sandburg's rich pieces, a sweetness come out of grime, seemed to inform all the drab and humdrum objects spread over the landscape before me. An event of great importance was taking place in this city, I knew. It had begun when first Dr. Wolle returned from Europe with the intent of performing the great Mass each year, and it was, surely, to remain for many years to come, in process of accomplishment. It was an event such as takes place when directly next a certain color its complement is set. Such an harmonic opposition was created by the beautiful presentation in this place of the works of Johann Sebastian Bach. For in the music of Bach there lies in one of its most powerful expressions the principle completely complementary to the principle of our civilization. No man, it seems, has been more replete with the giving virtue than was the cantor of the Thomasschule. For Bach, there was no life of man outside the state in which men give to each other, and, in taking from one another, give each other the power to donate themselves ever more copiously. Man was a fallen thing outside that state he knew; alone in that community which exists when two or more touch, does man achieve the stature of man.

That principle was not adapted from without. It was the manner of being of the man; the orientation of his spirit. It may even have been never more than half-conscious in him. Perhaps he reflected very little in the philosophic sense, and never formulated his religion. Certainly, it is known that when he wanted to state the theory of the fugue, he could do no more (nor less) than write the twenty-four preludes and fugues of the first book of the "Well-Tempered Clavichord"; and other abstract thought was probably as difficult for him. But that such was his understanding of life, his work seems readily to prove. Such an attitude seems to condition the "form" of the "St. Matthew Passion." Here, there is but one actor, and it is man. It is not man alone at the time of the Crucifixion. It is man at all time, Adam and Bach and Charles M. Schwab. It is the corpus all

men together form, and which lives and dies as they
touch or as they separate. There is no fixed division
between the presenters and the public; the public rises
and joins in the chorales. In part this "form" was inherited by Bach from the Protestant service; but Bach
was not the man to accept anything out of conventionality. When he, Evangelical of the dark days before
Illumination, wanted, he wrote Catholic Latin Masses, and
made the art of music, the art of Couperin as well as of
Buxtehude, over to accord with his ideas. No, Bach had
something to say about life. The assemblage of singers
and auditors are together the crucified and the crucifiers.
It is they yell the hateful words, and hear them as they
fall on the ears of Jesus. It is they who suffer, and take
the body down and lay it to rest, and through the sight
of their own crime are turned to God, and offer themselves in contrition wholly to him.

Is not precisely such an attitude towards life expressed
by the very polyphonic nature of Bach's art? Are not
his prodigious counterpoints the results in a musical mind
of the vision in nature of opposing objects combining and
giving life to each other; and its attendant hearing of a
polyphonic universe? Certainly, polyphony is the art
which achieves unity and power through the simul-
taneous combination of two or more individual voice-
parts which never forfeit their independent interest, and
still create a harmony. Certainly, although Bach may
not have made a more perfect music than did the
madrigalists, he created one no less wonderful than
theirs and increased the physical apparatus of music
by including the sounds of instruments in his immense
contrapuntal edifices. So, it seems not too overweening
to presume that this peculiar feeling about man grew
together with his technique; and that the two interplayed

and increased each other until the gigantic soul that was Bach's had fleshed itself in notes.

But down in Bethlehem; in every American town, how many are there who know what Bach knew? Is not well-nigh the whole of American civilization builded on the completest ignorance of that truth; established on the principle that the welfare of man lies in each one playing always for himself and never against himself; in each one taking what he can and in giving as little as possible? Is it not vowed to the great game of getting the other fellow's money? Of those who really believe that it is not in what each holds, but in what all share; in what lies between man and man that the wealth of the world consists, there are very few. And yet, of all those millions engaged in supplying themselves with material goods, there is not one who truly believes in what he is doing one-half as much as Bach believed in the usefulness of making music. Not any of the steel-workers down in the iron sheds of the Bethlehem steel plant where the great iron cranes go down the ceilings like sunset down the sky. There may be a sense of power flowing from the enormity of the physical apparatus they handle. But faith there is none; for men who have faith look not so sad and gray even in hellish labor. Nor does the millionaire who heads the company believe in his job as Bach believed. Bach gave no power into the hands of his antichrist. But this man helps support what is indeed the very devil to his god. For he, no more than the last of his workmen, finds satisfaction in his devotions paid his deity.

And what I had seen, then, was a sort of momentary turning of the tide of life. I had seen a vast churchful of hands grasping blindly for the unknown thing with-out which a material-rich civilization cannot commence

to live. I had seen under the direction of one American
a little more advanced than the rest, beauty issue forth
from common American bodies. I had seen a thousand
people unwittingly confess themselves to the distant
power. And as I went again towards the church it
seemed to me that something had happened not alone to
me and to an odd thousand of singers and listeners; it
seemed that through the far, subtle complex interrela-
tions of folk something had happened to the whole of
the land; and that in some mysterious fashion all of
America for an hour was standing, hands groping upward, merged in that ceremony.

August, 1922.

Alice Miriam

"FEU DE JOIE" was the last of the group of Szymanowski's songs chanted by Alice Miriam the rare evening I heard her. And, long before the day a few weeks since when I was told of her death; ever, indeed, since the fleeting instants in which she had caroled out the abrupt, exclamatory tones of the ecstatic musical moment, she had been curiously, deliciously, blent in my memory with the quality of the delicate song itself. It seemed it was herself, with her hectic, birdlike, tense-strung body, her high, thrilling, almost shrilling voice, that was the little ephemeral bonfire. During the brief while the white-shouldered slender girl in her clinging peplus had swayed before the blue-hung stage of the Town Hall, producing the startled joyous tones prescribed, it was to me as though something were happening within her spirit that was like the crackle and burst of ignition. She warmed the hands and dazzled the eyes and made flare the heart with her performance, as the twisting sword felt by the composer when he wrote.

Into the midst of the concert which preceded the performance of Carpenter's "Krazy Kat" ballet she had stepped as a sudden tentative streamer of flame snaps erect out of ash and half-charred logs. She was the artist. Before her there had come and gone people pathetic each in a different fashion; edges a little eaten into; talents wasting themselves in a sort of perverse asceticism upon objects not quite worthy of them. And after her there were to come others equally dry of palm. But Alice

275

Miriam had song in her. She had but to lift her voice, and after all the cloying syrups and bonbons, there was before one fine wheaten bread into which one might bite. She had found the medium through which she might give the charming gift of her spirit. The group of Szymanowski's songs—"A la Lisière du Bois," "St. François," "Feu de Joie" were three of the five she held to the baptismal font —are among the most individual and poetical and nicely synthetized of the recent compositions of the diffident and exquisite Pole. What is most apart and fine in his oblique nature seems to have been expressed almost in spite of itself in these brief instantaneous creations of mood. Szymanowski has written no music less external, more from his heart. These songs are the record of sudden searing touches upon a nature most often diffident and cool and withdrawn. They are full of shy whispering emotion, like to the sudden magical fall of a finger of evening light upon some bit of familiar boscage. A few notes, most often like the abrupt involuntary tones pressed from the breast by sudden instants of joy and ecstasy, fix the mood. We feel an event in the rapid breath of life upon the lutestrings of the nerves.

And Alice Miriam was herself those bits of elusive, rapturous life as she stood swaying above the piano placed at her feet in the orchestra pit. She had at the keyboard Allan Tanner to help her with his art lift the songs into light; but it was she herself out of her own rare spirit that made of the five pieces the tiny unforgettable summits. For the brief minutes she sang, there must have been nothing in the whole world before her save the Szymanowski music. There must have been nothing in her for that little while save the wish to make it flutter out into the hall. In her own experience she found those incandescent moments. Her gestures were a dancer's; once it was as though she were trying to make the long line of a naked shoulder carry out to the audience her intention. She was herself the ineffably sweet and worshipful soul of the Umbrian saint in its flowerlike adoration of the daintiness of earth; and as she crooned the almost sexless tenderness of the music, there seemed a sudden irradiation of the pale aureolas of the Italian primitives about her girlish head. And, last, she became an image of the bonfire, flaring with it as its tongues licked upward about the subservient wood, snapping and scattering joyous sparks of tone into the blue of night.

What must have helped fix the image of the bonfire on that of the girl standing white-shouldered above the grand piano was the furtive glimpse of her history given me by a gossip directly after her performance was at an end. That, too, brought to mind a sudden conflagration. My gossip had known her some ten years since as a prim timid little music-student from the American provinces; "the most mousey and whaleboned of little things." Later, it seems, she had gone in despair to Lago Maggiore; and there the director of an itinerant grand opera company had become interested in her. This man it was, my informant pretended, who had produced her talent. Then —suddenly, she had been engaged by the Metropolitan, and had appeared in New York, a very triumphant swan, a victorious personality, grown out of the Quakerish sparrow.

Again, the second and last time I saw her, on the afternoon on which she sang one of the two solo parts in Sam Thewman's "Der Abend," the image renewed itself. It was in vain she tried to give herself in caroling the dubious stuff. Though the composer in the conductor's stand tried to help matters out by assuming every now and then the pose of the descending sun-god in the large

of men who felt themselves somehow present in the elemental things they saw; who perceived their own sap
mount in the writhing tree and their own lust chase
through the wind-swept sky; and in their music drama-
tized the battle of the elements, the combat of man and
nature, the war of man with man. Bach seems to have
made organ toccatas in a kind of Dionysiac sympathy with
the roaring cosmos. Haydn seems to have been in the
peasants when they danced under their Austrian trees; to
have moved in music much as they swung and hopped on
the grass. Beethoven felt himself in all his rude strength
in the forest, the waters, in the crashing of the thunder,
and the falling of timber; the Waldstein sonata tells us
that he felt himself both in formless nature and man's
metaphysical mind, and knew vain the hope of ultimate
reconciliation. Something male and aggressive and active
seems in these men to have been moved on to a spiritual
from a physical plane: and to have returned again as the
disembodied breath of captains and pioneers and seafarers
into the primitive battle of men and things.

Franck's music brings us into the beam of another
light; to the world of a sunken sun. It is into an interior
that we tread with him, into a warm enclosed place; and
the light that suffuses the space between the walls is like
to the mild glow of the stilly lamp. The outer world has
become quiet and far in this room. It is present; all the
gigantic shapes that Bach and Beethoven saw are here,
too; but they have been changed in their nature, become
of a different substance. They have become, miracu-
lously, subject; they have become of the stuff of the
human soul. It is as though Franck, instead of feeling
himself out in things, had felt them all, earth and winds
and waters, enclosed, contained within his own breast;
and had felt the battle-place, the ultimate fighting-ground

of the universe, to be the terrain of his own heart. It was there and not outside, as it seemed, that all things took place. Franck is essentially subjective when he is most fine. What utters itself in his music resembles almost always the plaintive human tone. The clarinets, the English horn, the broad bass, sing with an accent curiously close to the human. He is lyrical where others have been most objective: in the framework of the symphony. Always, it is an individual life; the grief, the tragical abasement, the breaking of the personal will, of the little organist of Ste. Clothilde that speaks to us from orchestra and string quartet. He brings us midmost into his own life, reveals to us the long periods of acute moral suffering that were his; the march of pain through the mind, the sudden welling of tears in the baked waste lands of the heart, the bowing of the head before the divine will, the sweetness of peace retasted. His expression is essentially contemplative, feminine, and Christian. His strength is the strength of passive endurance, of humility, and gentleness.

The pile Franck raised opposes to the great masculine monuments of his predecessors a nobility not much smaller than theirs. The works of his last period record vision of the world rooted in a great heart, and expressed with all the serenity and tenderness stored there. Franck's understanding of life came at last to transcend utterly the conventional Catholicism of his day. Rolland is right: Franck saw the Christ, saw him in the light of his own experience. His savior is the Christ of the humble; pitiful of those who in this world suffer for the sake of justice and truth; a tender, childlike, almost oriental apparition. And, since he was so truthful in his own life, Franck's music expresses something of what is in all men. He is the singer of the inward agonists; of

must remain temporarily unanswered, of this we can rest
assured: the question has reality. Out of some subcon-
scious realm the best of these compositions do come.
They possess the vibrancy, the warmness, of matters made
not in the head, but down in the darkness of the bowels
and the reins; and with the intuitive man. It is the earth,
black and gritty, that swims up to us in them; not shut
casements and drawn portières and the airless state of
objects manufactured in the brain. They are natural
things; and could have grown, seconds, sevenths, ninths,
and other modern refinements notwithstanding, in fields
with the corn. We know where they put us, from the first
bars; and thank them, as we thank all music, with the
full blood.

The movement is outside the conventional patterns.
The little pieces have laws their very own. Brusquely,
naïvely, gnomishly, they commence, folksong and raffiné
at once, and go their free and whimsical way. They hang
well; they are simple, thin-voiced, and solid at once; they
hang by inherent and individual weights. Something determined and very sure of itself pushes them along.
Whatever it may be, it remains perfectly conscious of
much musical culture. It hears rich complex tone-
clusters, right hand in one key, left in an unrelated other;
adventures intrepidly in harmonic walks. But, withal, it
pipes along with a sort of nonchalance, like a child performing a two-fingered improvization, impish in humor
oftentimes. Rhythms run free, beat and clatter and
modify themselves to their heart's content. Rhythm for
us is "Petrushka" and the "Sacre," and some of Bloch
and Ornstein. And it is Bartók, too. The Hungarian's
patterns are smaller and slighter. The heavy bulk of a
dynamo man is not on them. Yet, his, also, belong to the
sacred band. They, too, are fullest play, record of

coördinated faculties, dictated by no Malipiero and Cyril Scott sophistication. The Pucks have it their naughty way in the scherzo of the second string quartet. Even when he is very childish, as he is in his Sonatina, the rhythms are spontaneous and unexpected.

And, in a dozen different figures and ideas, Bartók produces and affirms and develops a consistent individual color. On the piano, in the strings, he remains darker woodwind. He grunts nasal and portly, like bassoons, over his quaint intervals. When he sings lyrically beautiful, it is with a voice whose timbre recalls the English horn and its dark, penetrating, medicinal hues. One of the memorable moments of the second quartet occurs at the close of the scherzo; and there, it is the tones of clarinets and oboes and not of violins, which rise off the instruments. Sometimes, a grotesquerie seems to dictate these sounds speaking the nether gut. As often, more often, ideal moods make use of them. Certain composers, Schumann for example, are tenors always; in the bass, in the treble. They are always high in the chest. Others, whatever the range in which they find themselves, are baritone and color of snuff. Bartók is one of these.

Immediately, too, he is in between everything. The most of the "Esquisses" and "Bagatelles" are no more than a pithy page or two in length. A line here, a line there, suffices the composer. But they are white in heat. Something broke out under dire necessity in them, and said what it had to say in the concentrated form born of passion. You can not manufacture such subtly-moving poignant things: all essence like the third "Bagatelle" and "Elle est morte" in the "Esquisses." Either they are cast up out of lava-like experience of grief, or not produced at all. The third movement of the second quartet is the shortest of three short movements; but in a small space,

us; a limitation which, because of the marvelously new-
colored sparks already struck out of him, we heartily
wish wiped out entire.

Great sun Moussorgsky, shine down upon your
progeny!

April, 1923.

New German Music

I

BRIEF but terrible was our orgy of musical witch-burning during the war. It was in vain that well-intentioned people sought to preserve for the musical public the pleasure of hearing during the trying days the works produced by Germans in the last fifty years. It was in vain that Dr. Henry Van Dyke wrote that most German composers, Chopin and Beethoven in particular, were not Germans at all, but Jews resident in the Fatherland; seeking by this really brilliant piece of sophistry to save the situation for music-lovers. The best-laid plans went the way of many other best-laid plans. I know of a number of earnest souls who proposed to the authorities original schemes whereby modern German music might be robbed of its more insidious propaganda and be made palatable to full-blooded Americans, red, white, and blue; and were granted not even a hearing.

One of these schemes, indeed, was so ingenious that it deserves to be preserved for future use. "No more than a few changes in the words or in the business of enemy choral or operatic works," so wrote its serious-minded young author, "need be made to draw the sting of propaganda. For example: in the Ninth Symphony, let there be substituted for the words

Seid umschlungen, Millionen,
Diesen Kuss der ganzen Welt!

293

the words

> And we're going to show the Kaiser
> What those Yankee boys can do!

Or, in 'Tristan und Isolde,' let Isolde, instead of waving Tristan on with the usual white scarf, display a large American flag.   In 'Die Meistersinger,' Junker von Stolzing could be made to win the crown of Master and the hand of the fair Eva by singing, not the Prize Song, but 'The Star-Spangled Banner.'   The Rosenkavalier might be made to present to the affianced, in place of the silver rose, a Liberty Bond; while Salomé could demand as her reward that the head of either Nicolai Lenin or Senator La Follette be brought to her in a silver dish.   In this way eminently patriotic spectacles could be made of these works, and a victory gained over the most insidious Teuton snares."

But not even this spirited proposal was considered. No compromise could be effected.   There were too many people about suffering from painfully suppressed German ancestry.   There were others, not descended from Germans, who, nevertheless, on hearing a song of Brahms sung in the original, found themselves wondering in spite of themselves whether it was really possible that the People that had Produced such Beautiful Music could really all, all of them, be so wicked as the Quirites averred them.

Also, there were many people who had been finding the music of Beethoven and Wagner and Strauss "perfectly wonderful" with a slight though sometimes scarcely perceptible degree of effort.   Consequently, to the stake and to the lamp-post this stuff must go.   Into too many ears is poured its subtle insidious promptings.   Too many people felt that in some manner it contained the most subversive power; that its every note was charged with baleful suggestions and treasonable ideas. There was something black and awful about it, and it were best taken out of hearing.

Besides, were not our allies haranguing us and bidding us fling away forever this monstrous mess? Was not the eminent French composer Camille Saint-Saëns urging us to banish forever out of our hearts the love of the accursed fraud Wagner, and to bestow our affections instead on the safer modern French school composed of Reyer, Massenet, Gounod, Bruneau and of our humble servant, Camille himself? Was not D'Indy, from out the Gothic shadows of the Schola Cantorum, also invoking us to discard all German influence, as he himself had so rigorously done all his life, and turn instead to the French symphonists? And we could scarcely permit them to feel us greater slackers than they already did. So the way of all witches, wizards, conjurors, sorcerers, enchanters, succubi, incubi, seditionists, subversionists, insurrectionists, and all other satanic sowers of insidious enemy propaganda, modern German music went; and its place knew it no more.

And to-day, now that the daughters of the North German Lloyd and other persons have removed their ban from off it, and the opera and the orchestras and one or two singers not afraid of adding a difficult and original song now and then to their repertories, have commenced again to give us specimens of it, we find ourselves obliged to orient ourselves in a situation much altered. It was for the course of only a very few years that we were shut off from the minds of those who were making move—or seeking to make move—the musical art of Germany. Yet, those few years appear to have been the dividing line between two eras of music. There is a poem of Guillaume

Apollinaire's which describes his trip back from the Norman coast to Paris the night of the black thirtieth of August; at the end of the journey, he tells us, he set foot in a world different from that in which he had commenced his passage; something of the same feeling he must then have had, comes over us as we touch again the music of contemporary Germany. For if we have not set foot on new land, we have most decidedly left a familiar and old.

We have sailed from the land of Strauss. That is what the rising of the smoke-curtain shows us first of all. It is a twice-told tale that Strauss was never in satisfactory measure the real right thing. Nevertheless, he was the day. The Kaiser was a tone-poem by Richard Strauss; shining armor; externalized power; "Ein Heldenleben." Even the dreamy close came true. Particularly in his defects, the musician recorded his world; its desire for bigness; its want of unity and style. And now, he is no longer to-day. The festival of his compositions given under his direction in New York during the winter of 1921-1922 placed the star-ypointing pyramid upon his remains. He has gone to join the fathers of the tonic church in Abraham's bosom. What was good in him lives after him; but what is good in him is not the new, the unformed, the nascent thing which we require to hear. It sounds to us no more radical and novel and unhoused than the music of Schumann must have sounded to those whose ears were pierced by the chords of "Till Eulenspiegel." The stage is cleared. It is the hour of the new man, if new man there be in Germany.

These be years of wilderness-wandering. We have been given to hear the work of a number of composers; have seen a number of interesting attempts to create new values in musical form; but we have met only a single talent sufficiently fresh-minted to assure us the art of music is not decadent in Germany. The sun of Strauss may have set; no other luminary as large has risen to take his place in the firmament. Of course, we have not as yet been given to hear the music of a number of composers of whom there is some talk. Pfitzner and Schreker remain almost unknown; the fact that they write for the lyric stage, and that the Metropolitan Opera has not as yet given a work of either of them makes us to suspect they are composers of some merit. But, to judge directly from the works we have heard, the new generation, with a single exception, does not seem to be composed of very promising material. And, in a way, it would be amazing if it were to be found other than what it is. Musical art has a way of persisting even amid the thunders of falling worlds. There was playing and singing in the palace of Honorius as well as in the camps of the barbarian overtopplers of the western empire. But we may well question whether the stream of sound that issues at times such as these does not always resemble more the brook in August than in April.

II

An example of the directionless state of lyrical impulse in Germany was given us when the Philadelphia Orchestra performed the "Fantastic Variations on a Theme of Berlioz" by Walther Braunfels. Now, Braunfels has not up to the present been, strictly speaking, a post-Straussian composer. He, as well as Bischoff, Boehe, and other members of the group of Munich composers to which he belongs, have been a little more disciples than co-workers of the languid monarch. They have written program symphonies under his influence; tried to make orchestral novels about their own figures or that of Odysseus; or contrary, has with a really noteworthy prudence and middle-class virtue tried to make his work a theatrical success. The grandiose *Mutterleib* fantasy of Roden-bach's novel he has treated with a complete externality. When Puccini wrote "Tosca" and "Butterfly" he was not more eager to make every bit of it effective stage busi-ness; to give his singing-actors opportunities for histrionic display; to make every note "grateful" at the expense of the real significance of the action, than was this much acclaimed lad when he concocted "Die Tote Stadt." It was an extremely bright boy that Erich Korngold burst upon the world; for at the age of six, or perhaps of eleven, he could already imitate the manners of Strauss, Mahler, Debussy, and Reger all in a single composition. But what he produced was the thinnest of music. He was at his best when he wrote little waltzes richly harmonized like the "Valse d'Amour" of Reger and the "Rosenkava-lier" waltzes; and to-day he is at his best in gracile, sweet, unpretentious and philistine melodies, such as those he wrote for the performance of "Much Ado About Noth-ing." And so it is not surprising that we should find him not only not building beyond Strauss; but, while writing for the lyric stage capturing and vulgarizing the machinery of Straussian music—frosty "silver rose," harmonies and all—for the greater glory of the box-office and the pub-lishers of operatic potpourris.

IV

Only out of the two compositions by Arnold Schoen-berg which we have recently been given to hear, the "Five Pieces" for orchestra, and the melodrama "Pierrot Lunaire," has anything like the breath of a new force come to us.

The music of Schoenberg is concentrated as something squeezed with relentless might in a fist. It is seized; held; compressed. The water has been forced out. The softness and the non-essential have been forced out. What remains is skeleton-bone. Into a few small tins an enormous blasting-might has been stuffed.

All steps have been abbreviated. This mind has the tempo of the modern world. It recognizes approaching situations from a long way off. It comes quickly to consciousness; becomes aware with flashing quickness from the first low preliminary rustle and quiver in the nerves. It has the power of exceedingly rapid experience. It goes into things; and gets done with them again speedily. This is the great-surgeon technique. Schoenberg overleaps processes of relationship which to minds of slower tempi seem irreducible and fundamental. In what appear succession of dissonances, he hears a common pitch. Elements which seem to have no common basis he approaches to one another as though they were blood-brothers. The voices of his music have almost anarchistic independence. They seem to lie far out from the common center, on the edge of things. They are always like overtones of an implicit and unmentioned tone. But the links which connect, though they are fine almost to the point of invisibility, are formed of coldest durable steel. Great bales of substance, far-lying, have been condensed.

As this mind hears closenesses between far-lying things, so, too, it hears widths between close-lying chords. This music is compressed and almost painfully distended, too. Between two chords that lie so close the duller ear has difficulties in distinguishing them, it perceives iron resistances. So intense is the denseness of the harmony; so intense the density of the color, that the paintings of

Op. 7. And in the "Five Pieces," it utters itself with a poignancy become almost insupportable. A terrific tension expresses itself in the third piece, "Der wechselnde Accord"; in the slow, overlapping phrases, in the almost imperceptible changes of honey-sweet harmonies. One is reminded of one's first hearings of the second act of "Tristan," of the tower and murder scenes in "Pelléas." The chords twitch rather more than change. The orchestra murmurs with strange, contained, many-voiced passion. The music seems to lead us back into moments when tenderness became almost a searing flame, an agony; when the whispering voice was laden with glamor; and the touch of a hand thanked as no words can. With Schoenberg, it is either ecstasy of pain or ecstasy of pleasure; and the two are wellnigh one.

But it is a smothered desire that flares forth in this music. Schoenberg is the man without a machine. He is the creature of a time of dislocation. The machinery of life no longer coöperates with the human soul. It moves to a rhythm its own; and the mechanical things laugh down the poor human. We have no tools to work with. Tools, organizations, states, current ideas, socialisms, anarchisms, capitalisms, they no longer express the human being. They clutter the landscape. They fill the world with their noise and smoke and bulk. They make people do their will and misrepresent themselves. But they are of no use. The human soul cannot work with them. Still, it has not forged implements according to its needs. So the two things that ought to be harnessed run wild of each other. Strawinsky is more the thing that has run wild of man; the world in which no man exists; the mechanical rhythm that shouts its triumph over the microscopic human bug. He has tried to capture it for the imagination. The human torso of this time is in the music of

Schoenberg. He is the thing without arms, without legs, without organs of communication, without a phallus. He is the helpless quivering pulp; blindly stirring, groping, stretching. An almost immovable weight seems to lie upon his voice. And when it speaks, it seems to tear itself through shrouds; to come out as agony, as hysteria, even. The ecstatic voluptuousness of Debussy, by the side of this of Schoenberg, is like a thing safely delivered, safely carried across to its goal. It buds like flowers in the grass. Wagner's will, undercut as it was, seems free and direct by the side of this mortally wounded will. In these works, the cry of Amfortas and of the sick Tristan comes forth shrill, piping, broken. The tones are full of anguish; of anguish almost suffocated; but drumming and roaring underneath the blanket of silence.

Anguish speaks out of the sweetest dreams. "Eine blasse Wäscherin" is like a cool hand upon a pain-rent head; like the cool linens that release the body after states of exhaustion. It is out of some starvation-pit that the Pierrot yearns for Columbine. She is the drink of water to a black and leathern mouth. Moments of health are only moments of lessened sickness; moments when desire twists and takes a happier way, and suffuses the dried heart with dew; shivers of beauty that fall from the sky into his solitude at some street-corner and for a fraction of a second thrill the heart with unknown irretrievable bliss. For an instant, the past sings in the blood, and scatters some delicious old perfume, some pale gold light, into the gray air. More often, the pain speaks direct. Sometimes, as in the first of the "Five Pieces" it is merely the image of the states of sick presentiment the music brings up before us. A sudden twinge of fear in the woodwind. Another, more piercing quirk. Then, the dead weight of the orchestra plunged sudden in the

ness in the blood; and a quick extinction. A feeling comes
from somewhere; and for an instant the world is afloat
on moonbeams down to the safe still place of home. The
sun sinks slow; and the painful splendor of election, of
coronation, overwhelms; then flits away swifter than the
swallow. The witchery of a Chopin waltz intoxicates; a
phrase haunts and beckons mysteriously; but its magic
remains incomprehensible: and the summons it insistently
reiterates signals to something we have perhaps always unconsciously desired, but never seen more than faintly in
our minds or known or understood. All the wine and
hurt of vagrant, evanescent, unreasonable moods pours
over us. But it is only the wine one drinks with eyes; and
the hurt of shadow-swords that leave no fleshly wound.
Where the quiver and panic and exaltation come from, is
unknown. And they hardly connect at all with the forces
of the world, and substantiate themselves; but disappear
again into the arcana whence they came. All the election
and crucifixion of a savior goes on in the imagination of
Pierrot, sick subject of the wandering moon. He too is
apart from men and knows the sorrowing mother and the
piercing nails. But the elevation and crucifixion go on
only inside himself; and he remains indeed a white and
dreamy half-man, part poet, part dandy and part buffoon.

V

By the side of Schoenberg, the composer, there stands
Schoenberg, the transcriber, no whit less an exquisite talent than his twin. Depth and delicacy of feeling is in
them alike. The orchestral arrangements of Bach's
choral preludes, "Schmücke Dich, O Liebe Seele" and
"Komm', Gott, Schöpfer, Heiliger Geist" which Schoen-

berg made at the request of Conductor Stransky, are re-creations indeed. The two organ compositions have been genuinely refelt by the Viennese with reference to the contemporary orchestra. In the process of taking them into himself and reissuing them bathed in his own instrumental magic, he has further opened for us Bach's kingdom. Unlike certain other transcribers of Bach's pieces, he has not found himself obliged to alter radically the detail of the musical designs in translating the two poems into the idiom of a modern instrument. We are quite ready to believe the scholarly and imaginative program-notes of Mr. Lawrence Gilman when they assure us that practically all that has been added to the musical matter proper is "the three-note figure in contrary motion that occupies half a bar just before the fourth entrance of the choral melody in 'Schmücke Dich'; a similar one six measures further on; the filling out of chords and the octave doubling of parts; and a pizzicato violin figure, a flute trill, and a harp arpeggio that have no exact equivalent in the musical fabric of the prelude, though each of these slight elaborations is implied in Bach's music."

Schoenberg has preserved the delicate simplicity of the pieces, and has applied his own hand only in the recreation of the instrumental form. He seems to have sought to represent to himself the manner in which the tones sounded to the folk of the cantor's own time; and to have searched out of the armory of the modern orchestra the timbres and combinations capable of giving us sensations similar to those received by the congregation of St. Thomas' when its musician performed upon his wheezing, short-winded organ. And the music has been refelt with so much sympathy; Schoenberg has permitted Bach to play almost in his own naïve fashion with the textures

of our bands, with piccolos, English horns, bass clarinets,
double-bassoons, trombones, tubas, timpani, glockenspiel,
cymbals, harps, and celesta, that the spirit manifest in the
two pieces has defined itself with freshness, and stood
apart for us to see.

The two transcriptions restore to us again a sense of
the naïveté, the tenuosity, the seraphic lightness of Bach's
manner of feeling. The timbres of the modern instruments upon which his compositions are usually performed,
pianos, concert-organs, grand orchestras, manage in some
fashion to deprive his art of its innocence, its divine
allégresse, its levity of true greatness. They have made
us to visualize him always as a figure like to some of
Blake's ancient and titanic emanations; a sort of Los or
Urizen in a bagwig pedaling an organ with all the austerity
of a prophet and all the fury of an element. The heaviness of the sound prevents us from recognizing how often
in his moods Bach was "Jesu's playtoy" no whit less than
the young disciple of Francis for whom the holy Claire
first found the name. To this youthful, rapt, enthusiastic
state the instrumentation of Schoenberg restores him.
The preludes are become the frailest of orchestral fabrics;
quiet candle flames lit here and there in the orchestra; a
shine of mystic lights flitting across the ensemble of instruments. The coloring is rich and tender, but reserved.
Though the score requires nearly as many instruments as
that of "Salomé," the orchestra is treated somewhat in the
style of a concerto grosso, and the oppositions of the
tutti and single instrumental timbres preserve an archaic
flavor amid all the delicious sweetness and variety of
sound. In "Schmücke Dich," the choral melody is lightly
and warmly relieved by solo 'cello first upon a background
of muted and divided strings accompanied by woodwind,
the celesta, and the harp; later against horns, bass clari-

nets, violas, and double basses. So marvelously appropriate are the timbres found by Schoenberg that Bach the young lyric poet comes to be felt a personal presence. We seem to perceive him sitting at his instrument lost in moods of joy so still and so deep they threaten to burst his heart. The sweeping harp and violin arpeggios which open "Komm', Gott," perhaps the more genial and brilliant of the two transcriptions, recreate so marvelously well the mood which bore it that we seem to have a dazzlingly immediate access to the experience Bach was rendering; to hear the brushing of the wings of the divine visitor as he heard it when he gave from his breast the summons to Genius. And at the close, when the cymbals clashed and the triangle rang loud and bold above the resplendent full orchestra, and the flutes of ecstasy shrilled high, the childlike pomp of the baroque seemed for an instant to invade Carnegie Hall; and the laughing faces of plaster cherubs to flash out through the air; and behind the playing band of musicians there seemed to spread a sunburst made of pieces of gilt wood.

VI

There is no living German whose music we want more to hear than Schoenberg's. Each of his pieces that we have been given to hear is a separate and distinct experience; and we can guess what awaits us in the second string-quartet, in the monodrama "Erwartung," in the new "Kammersymphonie" and the oratorio "Die Jacobsleiter," and in the rest of his unknown works. Even though some of his compositions, the piano pieces Opus 11, the last of the five for orchestra, and certain numbers in the melodrama, refuse obstinately to come close; the greater portion of them grow upon one. The

early "Verklärte Nacht" pleases upon deeper acquaintance. At the first hearing of the work in its orchestral
dress, we perceive its resemblances to "Tristan." But at
a second and third, the resemblances, obvious as they are,
do not disturb us as they used. We are delighted with
the sincerity of the experience, the delicacy of feeling, the
daintiness of the violin color.

It is not as the quite freshest, the newest of musical
geniuses that we can regard Schoenberg, to-day even,
after we have learnt to respect him highly. Theoretically
the most advanced of all musicians, he is indeed by no
means the freest. Strawinsky's audacities are milder far
than the German's; and yet Strawinsky, particularly as
composer of "Le Sacre du Printemps," seems to have
caught something more completely alive and vibrant than
Schoenberg in any of his works. Schoenberg remains
somewhat Wagnerian even in the works produced by him
on the eve of the war. One hears an echo of the lyricism,
the sweetness, the manner of outburst characteristic of
Wagner, in the second of the five orchestral pieces, in the
instrumental interlude which precedes "Die Kreuze" in
"Pierrot Lunaire"; in the violin theme of "Heimweh."
It is not exactly vicious, the Wagnerism of Schoenberg;
it does not really spoil the early works. And in the later
works it is applied to new experiences, and becomes almost
a recreation. It merely holds his work in spots below
what might be the level of to-day; and keeps one from
completest satisfaction.

There is a strain of Brahms in Schoenberg, too. One
hears Brahms in the famous three piano pieces; the ghost
of Brahms in the final poem of "Pierrot Lunaire," with
its touching promise of recrudescence. Something of the
closeted atmosphere which sometimes irritates in Brahms

is in the modern, too. The smell of the lamp is never entirely absent from Schoenberg's music. Exquisite, sweet, and sultry as he can be, he remains as much the heir of Brahms and *his* heir Reger, as of Wagner and Chopin. A good deal of Schoenberg remains purest head-music; some of the delicate melodrama, even. "Enthaupt-ung"; "Der Mondfleck," with its double canon, are pro-digious upon the score-paper; but they do not impose in performance. The man has an unfortunate propensity to go wandering in the waste lands of abstraction. To some extent, he is the victim of German technical knowl-edge. The Germans, and the German musicians, know too much. They have all the technical knowledge and theoretical training of hundreds of years heaped on them; and when they come to compose, they cannot hear for the intellectual blanket upon them. The Russians and the French are more fortunate. They feel less with their minds; and are less inhibited when they come to do. But it is not alone German intellectual culture which must be held responsible for Schoenberg's paper-music, and for the want of freshest air one feels at moments in the best of his works. There must be some over-theorizing habit of mind in the man, threatening him always to snap his in-tuitional grip upon the universe.

And still, it is as one of the exquisites among the musi-cians that he comes to us. Since Debussy, no one had written daintier, frailer, more diaphanous music. The solo 'cello in "Serenade" is beautiful as scarcely anything in the new music is beautiful.

Life is enriched for us because we know this man is working, developing the expressivity of his art, entering new rooms with every piece. So powerfully has he im-pressed us, that we must confess ourselves very uncertain whether, when the mist has lifted from off the work done by him since the war, we may not discover the interregnum in German music past entirely; and discover the great line of German musicians moving forward again in him.

October, 1922—February, 1923.

THE END